Penguin Books

Utterly Trivial Knowledge: The TV Game

Utterly Trivial Knowledge:
The TV Game

Alasdair Riley

Penguin Books

Penguin Books Ltd, Harmondsworth, Middlesex, England
Viking Penguin Inc., 40 West 23rd Street, New York, New York 10010, U.S.A.
Penguin Books Australia Ltd, Ringwood, Victoria, Australia
Penguin Books Canada Ltd, 2801 John Street, Markham, Ontario, Canada L3R 1B4
Penguin Books (N.Z.) Ltd, 182–190 Wairau Road, Auckland 10, New Zealand

First published by Penguin Books 1987

Set in 9/11 pt Linotron 202 Century Schoolbook by
Rowland Phototypesetting Ltd, Bury St Edmunds, Suffolk

Printed and bound in Great Britain by
Cox & Wyman Ltd, Reading

Introduction

Ladies and gentlemen, put your hands together for a warm round of applause for Oscar Wilde. This warm and wonderful gentleman once said we 'should treat all the trivial things of life seriously, and all the serious things of life with sincere and studied triviality' and nothing could be more trivial than television.

Here are 1,350 questions, divided into 225 quizzes all devoted to television. Each quiz is divided into six categories: 1) Soap operas, 2) Personalities, 3) Drama, 4) Comedy, 5) American programmes, 6) Pot luck. If you answer most of the questions correctly, you probably have square eyes and are recommended to see an optician!

Now a quick word about each subject section:

1) *Soap Operas*: These are what most of us watch, and some even think that the characters are real. This leap of faith is not necessary to answer questions in this category which are restricted – purely because they are the most popular – to *Dynasty*, *Dallas*, *Coronation Street*, *Emmerdale Farm*, *EastEnders* and *Crossroads*.

2) *Personalities*: Such is the nature of the electronic beast that, while some people are born to be famous on television and some achieve fame through television, others have telly fame thrust upon them – and some people are merely famous for being famous. In every case in this category, the answer you are looking for is the name of a person.

3) *Drama*: This section makes only passing reference to the stuff we were taught at school or college, although *EastEnders* has earned its place on certain curricula. It covers the waterfront from Jim Bergerac in Jersey through *The Twilight Zone* to Minnie Caldwell's cat.

4) *Comedy*: This section covers most of what TV-entertainment producers consider to be funny. Questions range from sitcoms to comedians who do a brave job

attempting to put a little joy into our lives. As someone who once attempted to 'warm up' the audience for Tom O'Connor, I know just how brave.

5) *American Programmes*: This category covers a multitude of sins. Some American programmes sin so badly that there should be an Eleventh Commandment forbidding them from being anything other than a gleam in the eye of a misguided producer. However, where there's muck there's brass (variations of this bearded proverb have provided several TV-drama titles) and it is here that this compiler's prejudice towards series such as *Bilko* and *M*A*S*H* is to be found.

6) *Pot Luck*: Punch any other button, and you could come up with one of the questions in this category. So you need to know such essential data as Bet Lynch's middle name or which drama series had a fifth dimension beyond that which is known to man. Questions which don't really fall into any of the five previous categories are also to be found here and so are some of the trickier questions which boldly go where no other TV trivia quiz has gone before.

1

1. What was the name of Minnie Caldwell's cat in *Coronation Street*?
2. Who became a national institution with sporty catchphrases such as 'oop and under' and 'takin' an early bath'?
3. What is the Bellamys' address in *Upstairs Downstairs*?
4. What is the link between Lenny Henry, David Copperfield and Tracy Ullman?
5. What is the name of the Love Boat?
6. Who is an expert in Chinese in *The Colbys*?

76

1. What is the first name of Pam Ewing's adopted son in *Dallas*?
2. Pseudonymous script-writer Gerald Wiley is better known as which half of a famous comedy duo?
3. To whom does Napoleon Solo report in *The Man From UNCLE*?
4. *Bootsie and Snudge* was the spin-off of which popular comedy show?
5. Who is Matt Dillon's sidekick?
6. Who played the ragdoll in *Worzel Gummidge*?

151

1. Albert Square is in which imaginary London borough (*EastEnders*)?
2. Who first presented *World of Sport*?
3. Who plays Dutch detective Van Der Valk?
4. Which theatrical dame played Reg Varney's mum in early episodes of *On the Buses*?
5. Who are Old Timer, Jose, Don Pedro O'Sullivan and Professor Horatio Tucker?
6. Whose line is 'Who loves ya, baby?'

1

1. Bobbie.
2. Eddie Waring.
3. 165 Eaton Place.
4. *Three of a Kind.*
5. *Pacific Princess.*
6. Monica Colby.

76

1. Christopher.
2. Ronnie Barker.
3. Mr Waverley.
4. *The Army Game.*
5. Chester.
6. Una Stubbs.

151

1. Walford.
2. Eamonn Andrews.
3. Barry Foster.
4. Dame Cicely Courtneidge.
5. The Lone Ranger. (The other names are his pseudonyms when not wearing his mask.)
6. Kojak's (Telly Savalas).

2

1. What is the name of Joe Sugden's house in *Emmerdale Farm*?
2. Who always tops the Christmas ratings?
3. Who played Shoestring?
4. Who is the 'Che Guevara of Tooting'?
5. Whose line is 'Ten four – and out'?
6. Whose horses are Phantom and Tornado?

77

1. In *Dynasty*, who has been played by both Al Corley and Jack Coleman?
2. Who was the first host of the British version of *Candid Camera*?
3. Name the longest-running British police series.
4. Which British comic had a hit record with 'Funkie Moped'?
5. Name the cab company in *Taxi*.
6. *Pride of Our Alley* told whose story?

152

1. Name the newspaper in *Crossroads*.
2. Who invites contestants to 'come on down'?
3. What do Reginald Tate, John Robinson, André Morrell and Sir John Mills have in common?
4. Which comedy duo used to call themselves the Harper Brothers?
5. Who played Cannon?
6. Who was Britain's first Eurovision Song Contest winner?

2

1. Demdyke.
2. The Queen (in her Christmas Day broadcast).
3. Trevor Eve.
4. Wolfie Smith (Robert Lindsay) in *Citizen Smith*.
5. Broderick Crawford in *Highway Patrol*.
6. Zorro's.

77

1. Steven Carrington.
2. Bob Monkhouse.
3. *Dixon of Dock Green* (twenty-one years).
4. Jasper Carrott.
5. The Sunshine Cab Company.
6. Gracie Fields.

152

1. The *Castlewich Clarion*.
2. Leslie Crowther (*The Price is Right*).
3. All played Quatermass.
4. Cannon and Ball.
5. William Conrad.
6. Sandie Shaw.

3

1. In *Coronation Street*, what was Ena Sharples's favourite tipple?
2. Who had a 'schnozzola'?
3. Who first played Dr Who?
4. Whose creations are Captain Fred Scuttle and Professor Marvel?
5. In which city does *Gunsmoke* take place?
6. What do Parker the butler, Lady Penelope and Jeff Tracy have in common?

78

1. *Knots Landing* is a spin-off of which soap?
2. Who uses a tickling stick?
3. What is Patrick McGoohan's number in *The Prisoner*?
4. What is Miss Piggy's last name in *The Muppet Show*?
5. Who plays Detective Lance White in *The Rockford Files*?
6. A Norwegian Blue was a dead parrot in which comedy show?

153

1. Name the shop where Blake buys Krystle's jewellery in *Dynasty*.
2. Which scientist waved his arms around on *Don't Ask Me*?
3. What do Honor Blackman, Diana Rigg and Linda Thorson have in common?
4. Who is the poet in *Rowan and Martin's Laugh-In*?
5. Which hospital is known as St Elsewhere?
6. Who are Kelly Gerrett, Sabrina Duncan and Jill Munro?

3

1. Milk stout.
2. Jimmy Durante (his nose).
3. William Hartnell.
4. Benny Hill.
5. Dodge City.
6. Thunderbirds.

78

1. *Dallas*.
2. Ken Dodd.
3. Number 6.
4. Lee.
5. Tom Selleck.
6. *Monty Python's Flying Circus*.

153

1. Jensen's.
2. Dr Magnus Pyke.
3. John Steed's sidekicks in *The Avengers*.
4. Henry Gibson.
5. St. Eligius.
6. The original Charlie's Angels.

4

1. What is Seth Armstrong's job in *Emmerdale Farm*?
2. Who lost an earring while reading the news?
3. Who played a brickie in *Auf Wiedersehen, Pet* and went on to become a pop star?
4. How is Eddie McGinnis better known?
5. Who is the captain of the *Enterprise* in *Star Trek*?
6. Which I T N broadcaster's father invented the googly?

79

1. In *EastEnders*, what is the relationship between Vicki and Martin?
2. Which *Top of the Pops* host is a member of M E N S A?
3. Charles Dance played army officer Guy Perron in which series?
4. Who 'comes from Barcelona'?
5. Name the series starring a character called the Caped Crusader.
6. Which breakfast-T V interviewer did Margaret Thatcher call 'bonkers'?

154

1. What were the first words spoken in *Crossroads*?
2. Who began his career as the Mighty Atom?
3. Who were the two stars of *The Persuaders*?
4. Who played the neighbours of Paul Eddington and Penelope Keith in *The Good Life*?
5. In *Hill Street Blues*, who is always saying, 'Ma, I'll call you back'?
6. Which spy organization has its H Q above Del Floria's tailor shop in New York?

4

1. Gamekeeper
2. Angela Rippon.
3. Jimmy Nail.
4. Eddie Large.
5. James T. Kirk.
6. Reginald Bosanquet.

79

1. Martin is Vicki's uncle.
2. Jimmy Savile.
3. *The Jewel in the Crown.*
4. Manuel (Andrew Sachs) in *Fawlty Towers.*
5. Batman.
6. David Frost.

154

1. 'Crossroads Motel. Can I help you?'
2. Bruce Forsyth.
3. Roger Moore and Tony Curtis.
4. Richard Briers and Felicity Kendal.
5. Detective Belker.
6. UNCLE.

Q

5

1. Who got through endless hairnets in her role as *Coronation Street*'s battleaxe?
2. Which comic/quiz-show host's favourite sport is polo?
3. In which police series does Robert Beatty play a Canadian Mountie attached to Scotland Yard?
4. Which series is set in beautiful downtown Burbank?
5. What is unusual about Lieutenant Columbo's first name?
6. Who was the first woman to interview a British Prime Minister on television?

80

1. In *Dynasty*, when Krystle was kidnapped, who was sharing Blake Carrington's bed?
2. Who invited contestants to 'double your money'?
3. Name the award-winning drama in which John Hurt played a flamboyant homosexual.
4. Who is the mean landlord with a crush on his posh tenant, Miss Jones?
5. Whose is the voice of Charlie in *Charlie's Angels*?
5. Who loaded the crossbow in *The Golden Shot*?

155

1. In *Dallas*, who started as a hired hand and became a member of the Ewing family?
2. Who was the 'custodian of the questions' in *The 64,000 Question*?
3. Name Britain's first all-black drama series.
4. What do Rik Mayall, Adrian Edmondson, Nigel Planer and Christopher Ryan have in common?
5. Which police series features a Los Angeles cop with the catchphrase 'Just give me the facts, ma'am'?
6. Which rodent helped *TV-am* stay on the air before moving to the BBC?

5

1. Violet Carson (as Ena Sharples).
2. Ted Rogers.
3. *Dial 999*.
4. *Rowan and Martin's Laugh-In*.
5. We don't know it – it is never mentioned.
6. Noele Gordon.

80

1. Rita.
2. Hughie Green.
3. *The Naked Civil Servant*.
4. Rigsby (Leonard Rossiter in *Rising Damp*).
5. John Forsythe.
6. Bernie the Bolt.

155

1. Ray Krebbs.
2. Detective Superintendent Robert Fabian.
3. *Empire Road*.
4. *The Young Ones*.
5. *Dragnet*.
6. Roland Rat.

6

1. In *Emmerdale Farm*, who is the father of illegitimate Jackie Merrick?
2. Whose right arm operates the Australian-bird puppet which once mauled chat-show host Michael Parkinson?
3. Of which series was *Jason King* a spin-off?
4. Who ends his show with the words 'Goodnight, and may your God go with you'?
5. Which prisoner-of-war series stars Bob Crane?
6. How was John Eric Bartholomew better known?

81

1. What ailment does Lofty suffer from in *EastEnders*?
2. Whose catchphrase is 'How's about that then'?
3. Who played the all-knowing housekeeper Janet in *Dr Finlay's Casebook*?
4. Who said, 'Just like that'?
5. Which male character in *M*A*S*H* wears a dress?
6. Who was the BBC's first announcer – and then ITV's almost twenty years later?

156

1. Where was Noele Gordon standing when she said a tearful farewell to *Crossroads*?
2. Whose catchphrase is 'Hello, good evening and welcome'?
3. Who does Nerys Hughes play in *District Nurse*?
4. Who says, 'Rock on, Tommy'?
5. Who is the San Francisco detective in a wheelchair?
6. Whose false tooth popped out as he read the news?

6

1. Jack Sudgen.
2. Rod Hull.
3. *Department S*.
4. Dave Allen.
5. *Hogan's Heroes*.
6. Eric Morecambe.

81

1. Asthma.
2. Jimmy Savile.
3. Barbara Mullen.
4. Tommy Cooper.
5. Klinger.
6. Leslie Mitchell.

156

1. On board the *QE2*.
2. David Frost.
3. Megan Roberts.
4. Bobby Ball.
5. Ironside.
6. Kenneth Kendall's.

7

1. In *Coronation Street*, who chose to become a binman instead of going to university?
2. What is the nickname of disc jockey Gary Davies?
3. Who does Terence Alexander play in *Bergerac*?
4. Who says, 'All in the best possible taste'?
5. Who does David McCallum play in *The Man from UNCLE*?
6. Who played the organ in *Take Your Pick*?

82

1. Name Lady Ashley's job (*Dynasty*).
2. Whose catchphrases were 'swinging' and 'dodgy'?
3. Who does Keith Barron play in *Duty Free*?
4. Which comic used to be a milkman – and had a hit record about a fast milkman?
5. What is the nickname of the staff photographer in *Lou Grant*?
6. Which show ends with the words 'Watching us, watching you, watching us'?

157

1. In *Dallas*, who was blinded temporarily because of a gunshot wound?
2. Whose catchprase is 'I wanna tell you a story'?
3. Where do Arthur and Terry like to go for a drink?
4. Name the nasty inspector in *On the Buses*.
5. Who plays Jim Hardy in the Western series *Wells Fargo*?
6. Which show uses a 'clapometer'?

7

1. Curly Watts.
2. 'Medallion Man'.
3. Charlie Hungerford.
4. Kenny Everett.
5. Ilya Kuryakin.
6. Bob Danvers Walker.

82

1. Photographer.
2. Norman Vaughan.
3. David Pearce.
4. Benny Hill.
5. Animal.
6. *Game for a Laugh*.

157

1. Bobby Ewing.
2. Max Bygraves.
3. The Winchester Club.
4. Blakey (Stephen Lewis).
5. Dale Robertson.
6. *Opportunity Knocks*.

8

1. The Woolpack has a rival – name it (*Emmerdale Farm*).
2. How is Robert Davies better known?
3. Who has an antisocial sidekick called Lonely?
4. Which black-comedy series tells the story of Jessica Tate and her sister?
5. Joe Friday is the hero of which police series?
6. In *Falcon Crest*, who tried to shoot Angela at her wedding?

83

1. When *EastEnders* started, who moved into a dead man's room?
2. Whose catchphrase is 'Shut that door'?
3. Who does Brian Wilde play in *Last of the Summer Wine*?
4. Which series did John Cleese and his then wife, Connie Booth, both write and star in?
5. Name the chimpanzee in *Tarzan*.
6. What is the car in *Route 66*?

158

1. Who did Ann George play in *Crossroads*?
2. What is Jeanette Charles's speciality?
3. Who does Anna Carteret play in *Juliet Bravo*?
4. How is Ernie Wiseman better known?
5. Who plays Darren in *Bewitched*?
6. In *Brookside*, what did Petra and Theresa have in common?

8

1. The Malt Shovel.
2. Jasper Carrott.
3. Callan.
4. *Soap*.
5. *Dragnet*.
6. Julia (disguised as a nun).

83

1. Mary and Annie.
2. Larry Grayson.
3. Foggy.
4. *Fawlty Towers*.
5. Cheetah.
6. A Corvette.

158

1. Amy Turtle.
2. She's a lookalike of the Queen.
3. Inspector Kate Longton.
4. Ernie Wise.
5. Dick York.
6. Both committed suicide.

9

1. Name Hilda Ogden's cat in *Coronation Street*.
2. Who invited contestants to 'open the box' for almost twenty years?
3. Who stars as the power-hungry executive John Wilder in *The Power Game*?
4. Name the Morecambe and Wise signature tune.
5. Who is the arch criminal in *Hawaii Five-O*?
6. The Wilkins were a real family in which documentary series?

84

1. In *Dynasty*, who is Blake's half-sister?
2. Who was Britain's first black newscaster?
3. Which series takes place at the Marcia Blaine School for Girls?
4. St Swithin's Hospital is the setting for which series?
5. Who rides Scout?
6. Name the Australian actor who was the heart-throb doctor in *Emergency Ward Ten*.

159

1. Who was Sue Ellen's first husband in *Dallas*?
2. Who told us about the spaghetti harvest one April Fool's Day?
3. Name the Cockney detective played by Nicholas Ball.
4. Whose catchprase is 'Chase me!'?
5. What car does Starsky drive in *Starsky and Hutch*?
6. Who played Elliott Ness in *The Untouchables*?

9

1. Rommel.
2. Michael Miles (*Take Your Pick*).
3. Patrick Wymark.
4. 'Bring Me Sunshine'.
5. Wo Fat.
6. *The Family*.

84

1. Dominique Devereaux (Diahann Carroll).
2. Trevor McDonald.
3. *The Prime of Miss Jean Brodie*.
4. *Doctor in the House*.
5. Tonto in *The Lone Ranger*.
6. Charles Tingwell.

159

1. J.R.
2. Richard Dimbleby.
3. Hazell.
4. Duncan Norvelle's.
5. A 1974 Ford Torino.
6. Robert Stack.

10

1. What was the job of publican Amos Brearly's father (*Emmerdale Farm*)?
2. Who said, 'The trouble with Freud is that he never played Glasgow Empire second house on a Friday night'?
3. Who played the three pop singers in *Rock Follies*?
4. Which series had about thirty comics cracking almost 10,000 jokes?
5. How is Lou Ferringo better known?
6. Kenneth Tynan used a four-letter word on which show?

85

1. Who was found killed in the first episode of *EastEnders*?
2. Which ITN newscaster quit to help launch the BBC's daytime schedules with her own chat show?
3. What TV role do Roger Moore and Ian Ogilvy have in common?
4. Whose catchphrase is 'Ooooooooooooooookaaaaaaaaaaaaay'?
5. In *Star Trek*, Mr Spock's pointed ears are a characteristic of which planet?
6. Who infuriated former Prime Minister Harold Wilson by asking how much he was paid for his memoirs?

160

1. What cocktail is served to honeymooners at Crossroads Motel?
2. Who burst into tears on John Freeman's *Face to Face*?
3. Name the controversial series in which Susan Penhaligon plays a girl obsessed with her father.
4. In *Bilko*, Maurice Gosfield plays which inept soldier?
5. John Joseph Ryan is better known as which TV actor?
6. There have been several TV versions of the exploits of Sherlock Holmes and Dr Watson. What is their address?

10

1. Undertaker.
2. Ken Dodd.
3. Charlotte Cornwell, Julie Covington and Rula Lenska.
4. *The Comedians*.
5. The Incredible Hulk.
6. *Not So Much a Programme, More a Way of Life*.

85

1. Reg Cox.
2. Pamela Armstrong.
3. The Saint.
4. Lenny Henry.
5. Vulcan.
6. David Dimbleby.

160

1. Heart of Gold.
2. Gilbert Harding.
3. *Bouquet of Barbed Wire*.
4. Duane Doberman.
5. Jack Lord.
6. 221b Baker Street.

11

1. Name the mother of Terry Duckworth's illegitimate child in *Coronation Street*.
2. Whose trademark is a pink bow tie?
3. Which member of the cast of *Upstairs Downstairs* was partly responsible for originating the series?
4. *The Goon Show* was televised – true or false?
5. *Rhoda*, *Phyllis* and *Lou Grant* are spin-offs of which series about a bachelor girl working in a TV newsroom?
6. Who gave Terry Wogan a helping hand when he fell on his big TV first night?

86

1. How many storeys high is the Denver-Carrington building (*Dynasty*)?
2. Which novelist/critic left *What's My Line?* after a few months because she could not stand being a celebrity?
3. What was the faithless spin-off of *Budgie*?
4. Who played the children in *Bless This House*?
5. Who regularly beats Hamilton Burger in court?
6. Bob Geldof's father-in-law played the organ in which programme?

161

1. In *Dallas*, which road do you take to get to Southfork?
2. Who is the high-eyebrow presenter of the BBC's longest-running programme, which celebrated twenty-five years in 1982?
3. Whose boss is Spikings?
4. Who are the Dangerous Brothers?
5. Which top cop show stars real-life brothers?
6. *TISWAS* was a hit kids' show – but what did the letters stand for?

11

1. Andrea Clayton.
2. Frank Muir.
3. Jean Marsh.
4. True – once, in 1968.
5. *The Mary Tyler Moore Show*.
6. Elton John.

86

1. Thirty-five.
2. Marghanita Laski.
3. *Charles Endell Esquire*.
4. Sally Geeson and Robin Stewart.
5. Perry Mason.
6. *Stars on Sunday*.

161

1. Braddock Road.
2. Patrick Moore.
3. Dempsey and Makepeace.
4. Rik Mayall and Adrian Edmondson.
5. *Kojak*. (Telly Savalas and his brother, George.)
6. Today Is Saturday, Wear A Smile.

12

1. In *Emmerdale Farm*, who was Pat Sugden's first husband?
2. What's the real name of the Galloping Gourmet?
3. What is the name of the boatyard in *Howard's Way*?
4. Who changed his name from Jimmy Mulgrew?
5. Who is always saying, 'Book 'em, Danno'?
6. Which *Sale of the Century* hostess joined Crossroads Motel?

87

1. Name the twins in *EastEnders*.
2. What's the first name of TV cook Fanny Cradock's husband?
3. What do Ian Lavendar, Bill Pertwee, John Laurie and James Beck have in common?
4. What's the surname of Tom and Barbara, who bring pigs into their suburban garden?
5. In which soap do you find the *New San Francisco Globe*?
6. What was the long-running series *The Troubleshooters* first called?

162

1. Who was the *Crossroads* actor who was a regular in *Compact*?
2. What is the nickname of disc jockey Alan Freeman?
3. *Z Cars* is set in the fictional part of which city?
4. What's the link between Bernard Bresslaw, Alfie Bass and Bill Fraser?
5. *Criss Cross Quiz* was the British name for which American show?
6. Where is the Scottish soap opera *Take the High Road* set?

12

1. Tom Merrick.
2. Graham Kerr.
3. The Mermaid Yard.
4. Jimmy Cricket.
5. Steve McGarrett (Jack Lord) in *Hawaii Five-O*.
6. Sneh Gupta.

87

1. Pauline Fowler and Pete Beale.
2. Johnny.
3. *Dad's Army*.
4. Good (*The Good Life*).
5. *Falcon Crest*.
6. *Mogul*.

162

1. Ronald Allen.
2. 'Fluff'.
3. Newton, Liverpool.
4. *The Army Game*.
5. Tic Tac Dough.
6. Glendarroch.

13

1. Why did Mavis Riley change the name of her pet budgie in *Coronation Street*?
2. Who was the original presenter of *Name That Tune*?
3. Which series always began with the words 'Evening, all'?
4. Whose catchphrase is 'Hello, my darlings'?
5. Name the series about an unusual horse which talks only to its owner.
6. Which country scored zero points in the Eurovision Song Contest?

88

1. Who did Pamela Bellwood play in *Dynasty*?
2. Which bandleader's catchphrase was 'Wakey, wakey!'?
3. Which character says, 'Gizza job'?
4. Whose trademark was a fez?
5. Who calls his friend Kemo Sabe?
6. Which famous radio show was revived in *Bruce Forsyth's Big Night*?

163

1. In *Dallas*, who shot J.R.?
2. How is Maurice Cole better known?
3. Which powerful play about the homeless led to the formation of the charity Shelter?
4. Which comic said, 'Opportunity Knocks' ten years after it was axed by ITV?
5. What magic word – and the name of the series – turns a radio announcer into Captain Marvel?
6. In *Coronation Street*, what are the names of the Barlow twins?

13

1. It turned out to be female.
2. Tom O'Connor.
3. *Dixon of Dock Green*.
4. Charlie Drake.
5. *Mr Ed*.
6. Norway.

88

1. Claudia Blaisdell.
2. Billy Cotton.
3. Yosser (*The Boys from the Blackstuff*).
4. Tommy Cooper.
5. Tonto – it is his name for the Lone Ranger.
6. The Glums.

163

1. Kristin.
2. Kenny Everett.
3. *Cathy Come Home*.
4. Bob Monkhouse.
5. Shazam!
6. Susan and Peter.

14

1. What is the name of the village pub in *Emmerdale Farm*?
2. How is Michael Dumble-Smith better known?
3. Who played the character who lost an arm in *Jewel in the Crown*?
4. Who was the only girl in the original *Game for a Laugh* line-up?
5. Which top box-office star came to fame in *Rawhide*?
6. Who were the long-legged beauties who livened up *Sunday Night at the London Palladium*?

89

1. What do the EastEnders call their pub?
2. Who became famous for the command 'Walkies!'?
3. Who plays Adrian Mole's mum?
4. Name the army camp in which Sergeant Bilko rules the motor pool.
5. What is Dr Leonard McCoy's nickname in *Star Trek*?
6. Which *Brookside* actress was once Miss UK?

164

1. In *Crossroads*, who went to fetch a spanner and did not come back for six months?
2. Whose catchphrase is 'Nice to see you, to see you – nice'?
3. Who was the first American to star in a British TV production of a Shakespearian play?
4. Who was always saying, 'You are awful – but I like you'?
5. What is the nickname of Officer Renko in *Hill Street Blues*?
6. Who did Betty Alberge play in *Brookside*?

14

1. The Woolpack.
2. Michael Crawford.
3. Tim Piggott-Smith.
4. Sarah Kennedy.
5. Clint Eastwood.
6. The Tiller Girls.

89

1. The Queen Vic.
2. Barbara Woodhouse.
3. Julie Walters and, later, Lulu.
4. Fort Baxter.
5. 'Bones'.
6. Dinah May (Samantha).

164

1. Benny.
2. Bruce Forsyth.
3. Richard Chamberlain (*Hamlet*).
4. Dick Emery.
5. 'Cowboy'.
6. Edna Cross.

15

1. In *Coronation Street*, who was Alf Roberts's mayoress in 1973?
2. Who said the happiest news he had had to announce was Stalin's death?
3. What do Warren Mitchell, Dandy Nichols, Una Stubbs and Anthony Booth have in common?
4. Which comedy duo signs off with 'It's goodnight from me', 'And it's goodnight from him'?
5. Name Stefanie Powers's character in *The Girl from UNCLE*.
6. What do Peter Marshall, Pete Murray, David Coleman, Michael Aspel, David Jacobs and Terry Wogan have in common?

90

1. In *Dynasty*, what happened to Cecil Colby on the eve of his wedding to Alexis?
2. Who was the only original panellist to appear in the *What's My Line?* revival in 1984?
3. Who was always being called 'You dirty old man'?
4. Where did Dave Allen, Ted Rogers, Jimmy Tarbuck and Des O'Connor learn their trade?
5. What British show became *All in the Family* in America?
6. What was *Coronation Street* almost called?

165

1. In *Dallas*, what relation is J. R. to Bobby?
2. Which I T N newsman used his reporting background to write bestselling thrillers?
3. How were Clayton Moore and Jay Silverheels better known?
4. Which American show ended with the sound of two clapping hands?
5. Who plays the police woman?
6. Which *Sesame Street* character later hosted his own show?

15

1. Annie Walker.
2. Robert Dougall.
3. *Till Death Do Us Part.*
4. The two Ronnies.
5. April Dancer.
6. They have all been *Come Dancing* presenters.

90

1. He suffered a heart attack.
2. Barbara Kelly.
3. Steptoe (Wilfrid Brambell) in *Steptoe and Son.*
4. They were Redcoats at Butlin's holiday camps.
5. *Till Death Do Us Part.*
6. *Florizel Street.*

165

1. J.R. is Bobby's older brother.
2. Gerald Seymour.
3. The Lone Ranger and Tonto.
4. *Rowan and Martin's Laugh-In.*
5. Angie Dickinson.
6. Kermit the Frog.

16

1. Who does Ian Sharrock play in *Emmerdale Farm*?
2. Who replaced Selina Scott on *News At Ten*?
3. Who played the title role in *I, Claudius*?
4. Who are the two hecklers in *The Muppet Show*?
5. What happened to Klinger at the end of *M*A*S*H*?
6. Who was the human being in *Andy Pandy*?

91

1. In *EastEnders*, what does Dirty Den call his adopted daughter Sharon?
2. Who was a member of a group called the Humblebums before finding comedy success?
3. Which drama/documentary led to Saudi Arabia's breaking off diplomatic relations with Britain?
4. Who was dropped from the original quartet of *Not the Nine O'Clock News*?
5. Who is the newspaper proprietor in *Lou Grant*?
6. Which American private eye lives in a trailer?

166

1. Who spoke the first words in *Crossroads*?
2. Which newscaster refused $75,000 to take off her clothes for a girlie magazine?
3. What do *Sutherland's Law* and *Budgie* have in common?
4. Who play George and Mildred?
5. What's Kojak's brother called?
6. Which show stars Dusty Bin?

16

1. Jackie Merrick.
2. Pamela Armstrong.
3. Derek Jacobi.
4. Statler and Waldorf.
5. He got married (to Sun-Lee).
6. Maria Bird.

91

1. Princess.
2. Billy Connolly.
3. *Death of a Princess*.
4. Chris Langham.
5. Mrs Pynchon.
6. Jim Rockford.

166

1. Jill Richardson (later Jill Chance).
2. Anna Ford.
3. Iain Cuthbertson.
4. Brian Murphy and Yootha Yoyce.
5. Stavros.
6. *3–2–1*.

17

1. Who ran Gamma Garments for Spiros Papagopolous in *Coronation Street*?
2. Which newsreader high-kicked on *Morecambe and Wise*?
3. What do Anna Carteret and Jill Gascoine have in common?
4. Jim Davidson came to fame in which talent show?
5. Name the town in *The Little House on the Prairie*.
6. Name the popular bar in *M*A*S*H*.

92

1. What's the name of Alexis's company in *Dynasty*?
2. Which T V pundit did Muhammad Ali describe as 'not so dumb as he looks'?
3. Who do *Butterflies* and *Nanny* have in common?
4. Which comedienne is married to the Great Soprendo?
5. What is the name of the hotel in *Hotel*?
6. What are the dogs called in *Magnum*?

167

1. In which American soap do they meet at the Cattleman's Club?
2. Who is known as 'the singing pullover'?
3. Scratch is the canine star of which British nursing series?
4. Which show had the closing song 'Goodbye' – which went into the Top Twenty?
5. Who played Perry Mason?
6. The *Los Angeles Tribune* features in which popular American drama series?

17

1. Leonard Swindley.
2. Angela Rippon.
3. They both play policewomen.
4. *New Faces*.
5. Walnut Grove.
6. Rosie's Bar.

92

1. Colbyco.
2. Harry Carpenter.
3. Wendy Craig.
4. Victoria Wood.
5. The St Gregory Hotel.
6. The Lads.

167

1. *Dallas*.
2. Val Doonican.
3. *District Nurse*.
4. *Not Only . . . But Also*, starring Peter Cook and Dudley Moore.
5. Raymond Burr.
6. *Lou Grant*.

18

1. What job did Clifford Longthorn do when he left Emmerdale Farm?
2. Which presenter was axed after just one *OTT*?
3. What is the name of the British soap in which there is a dog called Tav?
4. What sitcom do Miriam Karlin, Peter Jones, Reg Varney and Sheila Hancock have in common?
5. In which popular series do you find Lotus Point?
6. What is the longest-running variety programme on TV?

93

1. In *EastEnders*, who did Angie Watts have a brief fling with while Den was in Spain?
2. How is Mrs John Thaw better known?
3. Tricky-Woo is the canine star of which British series set in Yorkshire?
4. Hannah Gordon and John Alderton played separated husband and wife in which sitcom?
5. Who are Mr Spock's parents in *Star Trek*?
6. Who had many half hours before committing suicide in Australia in 1968?

168

1. Who gave birth to a test-tube baby in *Crossroads*?
2. Who was chief prankster for the British version of *Candid Camera*?
3. What relation is Jim Bergerac to Charlie Hungerford?
4. Who are Spit and Cough?
5. What is Trapper John's last name?
6. Who played gormless Dr Moon in *Emergency Ward Ten*?

18

1. He became a cowman in Lincolnshire.
2. American actress Colette Hiller.
3. *Take the High Road*.
4. *The Rag Trade*.
5. *Knots Landing*.
6. *The Good Old Days*.

93

1. Tony Carpenter.
2. Sheila Hancock.
3. *All Creatures Great and Small*.
4. *My Wife Next Door*.
5. Sarek of Vulcan and Amanda Payson of Terra.
6. Tony Hancock.

168

1. Glenda Banks.
2. Jonathan Routh.
3. Former son-in-law.
4. Bob Carolgees's puppet dog and cat.
5. McIntyre.
6. John Alderton.

19

X 1. What character did Arthur Lowe play in *Coronation Street*?
2. Who became known as 'the man Britain most loves to hate'?
3. In *Upstairs Downstairs*, Mrs Bridges finally got married – to whom?
4. Whose catchphrase is 'It's a cracker'?
5. Who is the Bionic Woman?
6. Who is the man from UNCLE?

94

1. In *Dynasty*, what is Adam Carrington's middle name?
2. Which comic jokes that his wife buys his shoes in Harrods' boys department?
3. What does Maigret always do in the title sequence?
4. What do Scooter, Big Bird, Zoot and Grover have in common?
5. Who lives at the Bar 20 Ranch, Crescent City?
6. Who are Igor the bat, Spot the prehistoric beast and a Poe-quoting raven?

169

1. What is the surname of Jock and Ellie in *Dallas*.
2. Which TV personality is known as Whispering Grass?
3. Name the *Upstairs Downstairs* spin-off starring John Alderton and Pauline Collins.
4. What do Lenny Henry, Chris Tarrant, Alexei Sayle and Helen Atkinson-Wood have in common?
5. How many episodes of *Star Trek* were made?
6. What do the horses of Dale Evans and Annie Oakley have in common?

19

1. Mr Swindley.
2. Gilbert Harding (in *What's My Line?*).
3. Mr Hudson.
4. Frank Carson.
5. Lindsay Wagner.
6. Napoleon Solo.

94

1. Alexander.
2. Ronnie Corbett.
3. He strikes a match on a wall.
4. They are all Muppet characters.
5. Hopalong Cassidy.
6. They are pets of the Munsters.

169

1. Ewing.
2. Shaw Taylor of *Police Five*.
3. *Thomas and Sarah*.
4. *OTT* regulars who went over the top.
5. Seventy-nine.
6. Both are named Buttercup.

20

1. How did Peggy Skilbeck die in *Emmerdale Farm*?
2. Who starred in both *The Liver Birds* and *Are You Being Served*?
3. What do William Hartnell, Patrick Troughton, Jon Pertwee and Colin Baker have in common?
4. The Hotel San Remo is a popular setting in which series?
5. What is Mr Magoo's dog called?
6. Name the nightclub where J.R. got Afton a job.

95

1. Name the doctor who looked after Lou Beale when she got shingles in *EastEnders*.
2. How is Lynne Stringer better known?
3. Name the giant bubbles in *The Prisoner*.
4. Which show handed out the Fickle Finger of Fate?
5. In what are there 'eight million stories'?
6. What do Stratford Johns, Jack Warner, Stephanie Turner and Angie Dickinson have in common?

170

1. In *Dynasty*, what did Millie Cox choose as her stage name?
2. Which singer's trademark is a rocking chair?
3. Which is the village in *Dr Finlay's Casebook*?
4. Which comedy roles do Donald Sinden and Robert Guillaume have in common?
5. What is Sam Malone's nickname in *Cheers*?
6. Who was associated with the swingometer?

20

1. During childbirth.
2. Mollie Sugden.
3. All played Dr Who.
4. *Duty Free*.
5. Bowser.
6. The Stardrift Lounge.

95

1. Dr Legg.
2. Marti Caine.
3. Rovers.
4. *Rowan and Martin's Laugh-In*.
5. *The Naked City*.
6. All played TV cops.

170

1. Dominique Devereaux.
2. Val Doonican.
3. Tannochbrae.
4. Both have played butlers (*Two's Company* and *Soap*).
5. Mayday.
6. The political commentator Robert McKenzie – during elections.

21

1. In *Coronation Street*, what was Deirdre's surname before she married Ray Langton?
2. Which former Prime Minister hosted the chat show *Friday Night Saturday Morning*?
3. Which characters are the Professionals?
4. Whose catchphrase is 'Boom, boom!'?
5. Name the ranch in *The Virginian*.
6. Whose Dr Who trademark was a long scarf?

96

1. In *Dynasty*, what is Jeff and Kirby's surname?
2. Who said, 'Oi'll give it foive'?
3. Who plays Jemima Shore?
4. *George and Mildred* was a spin-off from which comedy series?
5. In *Dallas*, what is the Ewing ranch called?
6. What product was first advertised on British television?

171

1. In *Dallas*, what does J.R. stand for?
2. Which singer and comic has called himself 'the most hated man since Hitler'?
3. Who is 'er indoors?
4. Who says, 'I could crush a grape'?
5. What do the initials S W A T stand for?
6. Which American star was banned for saying 'pregnant' on T V?

A

21

1. Banks.
2. Harold Wilson.
3. Bodie and Doyle.
4. Basil Brush.
5. Shiloh.
6. Tom Baker.

96

1. Colby.
2. Janice Nicholls on *Thank Your Lucky Stars*.
3. Patricia Hodge.
4. *Man About the House*.
5. Southfork.
6. Gibbs S R toothpaste.

171

1. John Ross.
2. Des O'Connor.
3. Arthur Daley's wife in *Minder*.
4. Stu Francis.
5. Special Weapons and Tactics Team.
6. Lucille Ball.

22

1. In *Emmerdale Farm*, who is immediately recognizable by his bushy sideburns?
2. Which British TV-comedy star did an impression of Kermit the Frog when stopped for speeding?
3. Who used the phrase 'The world is your lobster'?
4. The Fenn Street Gang first appeared in which series?
5. Which character wears a monocle in *Hogan's Heroes*?
6. What have Eartha Kitt, Vincent Price, Joan Collins and Liberace shared?

97

1. In *Crossroads*, who moved to Canada after a test-tube baby?
2. Name the first presenter of *Tomorrow's World*.
3. John Thaw plays an investigative journalist in which series?
4. What do Gerald Wiley, Jonathan Cobbold and Jack Goetz have in common?
5. Who played Rodney Harrington in *Peyton Place*?
6. Who makes Blake Carrington's suits (*Dynasty*)?

172

1. Where does Pauline Fowler work in *EastEnders*?
2. Who would be called Cheese if his grandfather had not changed his surname?
3. The Foundry Piscatorials Club features in which series?
4. Who are Hill's Angels?
5. Blair General is the setting for which medical series?
6. What do Glyn Worsnip, Kieran Prendeville, Paul Heiney and Chris Serle have in common?

22

1. Amos Brearly.
2. Freddie Starr.
3. Arthur Daley.
4. *Please, Sir*.
5. Colonel Klink.
6. They have all played baddies in *Batman*.

97

1. Glenda Banks.
2. Raymond Baxter.
3. *Mitch*.
4. They are all Ronnie Barker's writing pseudonyms.
5. Ryan O'Neal.
6. Brioni.

172

1. The launderette.
2. John Cleese.
3. *Eh, Brian, It's a Whopper*.
4. Dancers on *The Benny Hill Show*.
5. *Doctor Kildare*.
6. They are all former sidekicks of Esther Ratzen on *That's Life*.

23

1. How did Ken Barlow's wife Valerie die in *Coronation Street*?
2. Which former wife of Frank Sinatra was in *Peyton Place*?
3. What does *Rumpole of the Bailey* call his wife?
4. Which comic was born David Tynan-O'Mahoney?
5. *Double Your Money* was based on which American quiz show?
6. Who was the long-serving host of *Criss Cross Quiz*?

98

1. In which American soap do you find the hotel La Mirage?
2. Who is the only human in *Fraggle Rock*?
3. Bertie is the upper-crust dog in which comedy drama starring Penelope Keith?
4. What is the name of the store in *Are You Being Served*?
5. Steve McQueen played a bounty hunter in which series?
6. What is Lady Penelope's car in *Thunderbirds*?

173

1. Who played Jenna Wade before Priscilla Presley in *Dallas*?
2. Who made the first maximum snooker break of 147 on TV?
3. Who plays the head of CI5 in *The Professionals*?
4. Which major solo comedy star was once one of the Black Abbots?
5. In which popular series, about a jet-setting couple, is there a dog called Freeway?
6. Who played Annie Walker's son Billy in *Coronation Street*?

23

1. She was electrocuted.
2. Mia Farrow (as Allison Mackenzie).
3. 'She who must be obeyed'.
4. Dave Allen.
5. *The 64,000-Dollar Question*.
6. Jeremy Hawk.

98

1. *Dynasty*.
2. Fulton Mackay.
3. *To the Manor Born*.
4. Grace Brothers.
5. *Wanted: Dead or Alive*.
6. A pink Rolls-Royce.

173

1. Morgan Fairchild.
2. Steve Davis.
3. Gordon Jackson.
4. Russ Abbot.
5. *Hart to Hart*.
6. Ken Farrington.

24

1. What breed of cow is most popular at Emmerdale Farm?
2. Who went from breakfast time to prime time to look through the keyhole?
3. Which series is set on Moon Base Alpha?
4. Who says, 'Have you ever been tickled Mrs?'?
5. Who played the San Francisco detective in a wheelchair?
6. Which footballer refused to appear on *This Is Your Life*?

99

1. Name the EastEnders' café.
2. Who was *Breakfast Time*'s Green Goddess?
3. Name the character who answered the phone with the words 'Arden House, Tannochbrae'.
4. What do James Beck, Ian Lavender, Frank Williams and Bill Pertwee have in common?
5. Max is the dog in which series about a scientifically reconstructed woman?
6. Who conducted the famous *Face-to-Face* interviews?

174

1. Which British soap opera is set in the village of King's Oak?
2. How was the third Baron Glenavy better known on TV?
3. Which series is set in St Angela's Hospital?
4. Whose dummies are known as Steve, Ali Cat, Tich and Quackers?
5. Too old to play Tarzan any more, Johnny Weissmuller brought which character to television?
6. In *Star Trek*, name the beautiful creature Mr Spock falls for on the ice-age planet of Sarpeidon.

24

1. Friesian.
2. Loyd Grossman.
3. *Space 1999*.
4. Ken Dodd.
5. Raymond Burr.
6. Danny Blanchflower.

99

1. Ali's Café.
2. Keep-fit expert Diana Moran.
3. Housekeeper Janet in *Dr Finlay's Casebook*.
4. *Dad's Army*.
5. *The Bionic Woman*.
6. John Freeman.

174

1. *Crossroads*.
2. Patrick Campbell.
3. *Angels*.
4. Ray Alan.
5. Jungle Jim.
6. Zarabeth.

25

1. What was Hilda Ogden's maiden name in *Coronation Street*?
2. Who was once introduced with the words 'Harry Commentator is your carpenter'?
3. Who does Patrick MacNee play in *The Avengers*?
4. Joan Sandra Molinsky brings near-to-the-knuckle laughs to TV under what name?
5. What does M*A*S*H stand for?
6. Who sang the theme tune for the Western series *Rawhide*?

100

1. In *Coronation Street*, who became caretaker of the Glad Tidings Mission after her husband died?
2. Which TV personality is in *The Guinness Book of Records* for tap-dancing?
3. In *Upstairs Downstairs*, who shot himself after being ruined financially?
4. Whose dummy is the drunken Lord Charles?
5. What is the name of the Cartwrights' ranch in *Bonanza*?
6. Who does Pegasus, the polo pony, belong to in *M*A*S*H*?

175

1. $2,000,000 in diamonds was the ransom demanded for what in *Dynasty*?
2. Who came to TV comedy fame after her Campari commercials?
3. Who was TV's first Just William?
4. Who played Bootsie and Snudge?
5. Who rides Diablo?
6. Who is the longest-surviving actor in *Coronation Street*?

A

25

1. Crabtree.
2. Boxing commentator Harry Carpenter.
3. John Steed.
4. Joan Rivers.
5. Mobile Army Surgical Hospital.
6. Frankie Laine.

100

1. Ena Sharples.
2. Roy Castle.
3. James Bellamy.
4. Ray Alan.
5. The Ponderosa.
6. Major Winchester.

175

1. Krystle's horse (which was kidnapped).
2. Lorraine Chase.
3. Dennis Waterman.
4. Bill Fraser and Alfie Bass.
5. The Cisco Kid.
6. William Roache (as Ken Barlow).

26

1. Name the two actors to have played Digger Barnes in *Dallas*?
2. Who used to say, 'And the next *Tonight* is tomorrow night'?
3. In *Dr Who*, what does Tardis stand for?
4. Who plays accident-prone Frank Spencer?
5. What's the surname of the chat-show host introduced by the words 'He-e-e-e-e-e-re's Johnny'?
6. What was the evocative theme tune of *Tinker, Tailor, Soldier, Spy*?

101

1. What are the first names of Annie Sugden's sons in *Emmerdale Farm*?
2. Who developed a love of archery while playing Henry V for TV?
3. Who was Dr Finlay and Dr Cameron's medical rival?
4. What's Arthur Mullard's catchphrase – and the name of his comedy series?
5. Name Richard Boone's character in *Have Gun Will Travel*.
6. What do Pete Murray, Jo Douglas, ex-boxer Freddie Mills and Jim Dale have in common?

176

1. Which British soap opera opened with a shot of a dying man?
2. Pop singer Peter Noone appeared in which British soap opera?
3. *The Forsyte Saga* was made in black and white – true or false?
4. Name the horse in *Steptoe and Son*.
5. Who did Clint Eastwood play in *Rawhide*?
6. Who is in charge of U N C L E headquarters?

26

1. David Wayne and Keenan Wynn.
2. Cliff Michelmore.
3. Time and Relative Dimensions in Space.
4. Michael Crawford (*Some Mothers do 'Ave 'Em*).
5. Carson.
6. 'Nunc Dimittis', composed by Geoffrey Burgon.

101

1. Jack and Joe.
2. Robert Hardy.
3. Dr Snoddie.
4. 'Yus, my dear'.
5. Paladin.
6. They have all been presenters of pop programme *Six-Five Special*.

176

1. *EastEnders*.
2. *Coronation Street*.
3. True – it was the last major British series in black and white.
4. Hercules.
5. Rowdy Yates.
6. Alexander Waverley.

27

1. In *Crossroads*, who died in a fire in a Spanish monastery?
2. Which TV cook was game for a laugh?
3. In which series did Susan Hampshire play Lady Glencora?
4. Who says 'fan-dabi-dozi'?
5. In which private-eye series does an answering machine open the programme?
6. Where did Elsie Tanner go when she left *Coronation Street*?

102

1. Who pulled out the plug when her husband made beer in the bath during a brewery strike in *Coronation Street*?
2. Who was the first newscaster on ITN?
3. Name the all-girl group in *Rock Follies*.
4. Which *Hi-de-Hi* star once had a very small part in *Coronation Street* as Alf Roberts's boss?
5. Name the rich family in *Soap*.
6. Which *Brookside* character was jailed for a crime he did not commit – despite a petition to Number Ten?

177

1. Name the Carrington butler who committed suicide in *Dynasty*.
2. Who has appeared in more Royal Variety Performances than anyone else?
3. What do Katy Manning, Mary Tamm, Lalla Ward and Jean Marsh have in common?
4. Who shut the door on his real name William White?
5. What is the code name of Starsky and Hutch's car?
6. What do the following have in common: 'Suicide is Painless', 'I Could Be so Good for You', 'Eye Level', 'That's Living Alright'?

27

1. Carlos, the Spanish chef.
2. Rustie Lee.
3. *The Pallisers*.
4. The Krankies.
5. *The Rockford Files*.
6. Portugal.

102

1. Hilda Ogden.
2. Christopher Chataway.
3. The Little Ladies.
4. Paul Shane (Teddy Boy Ted Bovis).
5. The Tates.
6. George Jackson.

177

1. Joseph (Lee Bergere).
2. Max Bygraves.
3. They are all former *Dr Who* girls.
4. Larry Grayson.
5. Zebra 3.
6. All are hit theme tunes for TV series (*M*A*S*H*, *Minder*, *Van Der Valk*, *Auf Wiedersehen, Pet*).

28

1. Who was at the wheel of the car which hit and killed Bobby in *Dallas*.
2. Who says, 'Hello, possums'?
3. Who was the first character to be seen in *Upstairs Downstairs*?
4. Whose catchphrase is 'Settle down'?
5. Who are Hoss, Adam and Little Joe?
6. County General Hospital is the setting for which American series?

103

1. In *Emmerdale Farm*, where did Dolly Skilbeck work before she married Matt?
2. Which chat-show host was hit by Grace Jones?
3. Jack Hedley played the senior British officer in which prisoner of war series?
4. Whose catchphrase is 'Slither hither'?
5. Which criminal organization is U N C L E's traditional enemy?
6. Which century is *Star Trek* set in?

178

1. Who ran away, taking Pauline's club money and forty fags, in *EastEnders*?
2. Why was Noele Gordon given her first name?
3. *Flamingo Road* is set in which American state?
4. Who lived at Railway Cuttings, Cheam?
5. What is Charlie's last name in *Charlie's Angels*?
6. What do Terry Wogan and Les Dawson have in common?

28

1. Katherine Wentworth (Morgan Brittany).
2. Dame Edna Everage (Barry Humphries).
3. Sarah, the under-parlourmaid (Pauline Collins).
4. Ken Goodwin.
5. Ben Cartwright's sons in *Bonanza*.
6. *Ben Casey*.

103

1. The Woolpack.
2. Russell Harty.
3. *Colditz*.
4. Roy Jay.
5. THRUSH.
6. The twenty-third century.

178

1. Mark Fowler.
2. She was born on Christmas Day.
3. Florida.
4. Tony Hancock.
5. Townsend.
6. *Blankety Blank*.

29

1. Which character did Roger Tonge play in *Crossroads*?
2. Who was Press Officer for the Isle of Bute before going into TV?
3. Magnum lives on which Hawaiian island?
4. Who is always saying, 'I'll get you, Butler'?
5. Name the actor who played Chicken George in *Roots*.
6. What do Tommy Trinder, Bruce Forsyth, Norman Vaughan and Jim Dale have in common?

104

1. Who is the former nightclub singer who went on to own a newsagent's shop in *Coronation Street*?
2. Who chairs *The Good Old Days*?
3. What was Britain's first daily TV serial?
4. On which programme did Freddie Starr, Paul Melba, Little and Large and Faith Brown make an impression?
5. Who is the Cisco Kid's buddy?
6. Who played Starsky and Hutch?

179

1. Who had an affair with the first Carrington chauffeur in *Dynasty*?
2. Which taxi driver became a TV personality after winning *Mastermind*?
3. What do Richard Chamberlain, Tony Adams, Andrew Cruickshank and Robin Nedwell have in common?
4. Which comic was once called the fifth Beatle?
5. Apart from Clayton Moore, who played the Lone Ranger?
6. Who liked his tea stirred three times anti-clockwise?

29

1. Sandy Richardson.
2. Selina Scott.
3. Oahu.
4. Inspector Blake (Stephen Lewis) in *On the Buses*.
5. Ben Vereen.
6. They have all compered *Sunday Night at the London Palladium*.

104

1. Rita Fairclough.
2. Leonard Sachs.
3. *Sixpenny Corner*.
4. *Who Do You Do?*.
5. Pancho.
6. Paul Michael Glaser and David Soul.

179

1. Fallon.
2. Fred Housego.
3. All have played TV doctors.
4. Jimmy Tarbuck.
5. John Hart.
6. John Steed in *The Avengers*.

Q

30

1. How did Pam try to commit suicide in *Dallas*?
2. Which singer became an international star after being the subject of one of Esther Rantzen's *The Big Time* programmes?
3. Which character did Bernard Hepton play in *Colditz*?
4. Who partnered Hattie Jacques in one of British comedy's most successful acts?
5. Name Pancho's horse in *The Cisco Kid*.
6. What did Isobel Barnett, David Nixon, Gilbert Harding and Barbara Kelly have in common?

105

1. Where in the Yorkshire Dales is the fictional location of Emmerdale Farm?
2. Who sang calypsos on the news and current affairs programme *Tonight*?
3. Who or what is K9?
4. Which rotund comic wrote a novel called *A Card for the Clubs*?
5. Who does James McArthur play in *Hawaii Five-O*?
6. What do Jerry Booth, Derek Wilton, Marcus Dodds and Victor Pendelbury have in common (*Coronation Street*)?

180

1. Where did Den take Angie on a second honeymoon in *EastEnders*?
2. Which bow-tied interviewer stood for Parliament as a Liberal in 1959 but failed?
3. Where is *Fame* set?
4. Which *Python* member was always saying, 'Nudge, nudge, wink, wink, say no more'?
5. What is Hawkeye's full name in *M*A*S*H*?
6. Who plays the title role in *The Fugitive*?

30

1. By jumping off a roof-top.
2. Sheena Easton.
3. The camp commandant.
4. Eric Sykes.
5. Loco.
6. They were regular panellists on *What's My Line?*

105

1. Beckindale.
2. Cy Grant.
3. Dr Who's robotic dog.
4. Les Dawson.
5. Detective Danny Williams.
6. They are all former boyfriends of Mavis Riley.

180

1. Venice.
2. Sir Robin Day.
3. The High School for the Performing Arts, New York.
4. Eric Idle.
5. Benjamin Franklin Pierce.
6. David Janssen.

31

1. Why did Meg go to jail in *Crossroads*?
2. Who started his career, aged 14, as Billy Breen, female impersonator?
3. What kind of car does Magnum drive?
4. Name the two spin-offs from Wendy Craig's *Not in Front of the Children*.
5. Who does Karl Malden play in *The Streets of San Francisco*?
6. Who are Huey, Dewey and Louie?

106

1. How did Alf Roberts's first wife, Renée, die in *Coronation Street*?
2. Which *Emmerdale Farm* star is the sister of Brian Rix?
3. Which cartoon strip (and we mean strip) does Glynis Barber bring to life?
4. What sort of guys are Rodney Bewes and James Bolam?
5. Which came first – BBC's *Breakfast Time* or ITV's *TV-am*?
6. Which British courtroom drama is set in the fictional town of Fulchester?

181

1. Who is the Carringtons' cook in *Dynasty*?
2. Whose catchphrase is 'Sincerely, folks'?
3. What is the name of the main street in Peyton Place?
4. Who did Robert Guillaume play in *Soap*?
5. Who charges $200 a day plus expenses?
6. Who did Raymond Francis play in *No Hiding Place*?

31

1. She was accused of dangerous driving.
2. Larry Grayson.
3. A Ferrari.
4. *And Mother Made Three, And Mother Made Five*.
5. Detective Lieutenant Mike Stone.
6. Donald Duck's three nephews.

106

1. In a car crash.
2. Sheila Mercier (who plays Annie Sugden).
3. *Jane*.
4. The Likely Lads.
5. *Breakfast Time* (17 January 1983 – by fifteen days).
6. *Crown Court*.

181

1. Mrs Gunnerson.
2. Hughie Green.
3. Elm Street.
4. Benson, the butler.
5. Jim Rockford in *The Rockford Files*.
6. Superintendent Lockhart.

32

1. What is J.R.'s favourite food in *Dallas*?
2. Which $6-million man had his nose smashed three times playing American football?
3. Who played Raffles?
4. Whose trademark is a giant leek?
5. John Hart and Clayton Moore both played the same Western hero in which series?
6. Who was originally cast as *Dynasty*'s Blake Carrington?

107

1. In *Emmerdale Farm*, what was Jack Sugden's first book called?
2. Who was the first subject of *This Is Your Life* in Britain?
3. In which city is *St Elsewhere* set?
4. Who was the Lad Himself?
5. Efrem Zimbalist Jr and Roger Smith were co-stars of which American private-eye series?
6. Which show featured a 'saggar-maker's bottom-knocker'?

182

1. Name the local newspaper in *EastEnders*.
2. Who was reading the news when a light-bulb exploded on her desk?
3. Name the series in which Peter Vaughan played the head of a south London family.
4. Who says, 'You'll like it. Not a lot, but you'll like it'?
5. Who plays Jason Colby?
6. By what name was *It's A Knockout* known internationally?

32

1. Miss Ellie's chilli.
2. Lee Majors (star of *The Six Million Dollar Man*).
3. Anthony Valentine.
4. Max Boyce.
5. *The Lone Ranger*.
6. George Peppard.

107

1. *The Field of Tares*.
2. Eamonn Andrews.
3. Boston.
4. Tony Hancock.
5. *77 Sunset Strip*.
6. *What's My Line?*

182

1. The *Walford Gazette*.
2. Jan Leeming.
3. *Fox*.
4. Paul Daniels.
5. Charlton Heston.
6. *Jeux Sans Frontières*.

33

1. In *Crossroads*, where was Malcolm Ryder supposedly burnt to death in a car crash?
2. Which well-endowed lady, known as 'the Hunchfront of Lime Grove', featured in Arthur Askey's shows in the 1950s?
3. In which series did Frank Finlay play an obsessed father who made love to his secretary in his daughter's bed?
4. Who's Odd Odes were a feature of *That's Life*?
5. What colour is Mr Spock's blood in *Star Trek*?
6. Who played Ken Barlow's younger brother in *Coronation Street* and went on to appear in *Brookside*?

108

1. What do Arnold Tanner, Sergeant Steve Tanner and Alan Howard have in common (*Coronation Street*)?
2. Who says, 'I've started, so I'll finish'?
3. Who played Sapphire and Steel?
4. Who was Ronnie Barker's cellmate in *Porridge*?
5. Name the palace used as a government HQ in *Hawaii Five-O*.
6. 'Beat the Clock' was part of which variety show?

183

1. How many rooms are there at the Carrington mansion in *Dynasty*?
2. Who says, 'Your starter for 10'?
3. What kind of car does Maigret drive?
4. Name the fictional TV station founded by a former Python.
5. NCC1701 is the identification number of what?
6. Which cult drama series ends each episode with giant bubbles appearing from the sea?

33

1. South America.
2. Sabrina.
3. *Bouquet of Barbed Wire*.
4. Cyril Fletcher.
5. Green.
6. Alan Rothwell.

108

1. They have all been Elsie Tanner's husbands.
2. Magnus Magnusson (*Mastermind*).
3. Joanna Lumley and David McCallum.
4. Richard Beckinsale.
5. Iolani Palace.
6. *Sunday Night at the London Palladium*.

183

1. Forty-eight.
2. Bamber Gascoigne.
3. A black Citroën.
4. Rutland Weekend Television (Eric Idle).
5. The USS *Enterprise* in *Star Trek*.
6. *The Prisoner*.

34

1. Who got married when *Dallas* started?
2. Who lives in Jersey when he is not living up to his reputation as TV's most travelled man?
3. In which series was Gerald Campion very big?
4. Name the sequel to *Porridge*.
5. Who did Kate Jackson play in *Charlie's Angels*?
6. Keith Fordyce hosted which pop show?

109

1. What is Matt Skilbeck's job in *Emmerdale Farm*?
2. Who is the Housewife-Superstar?
3. Who suffered agonies as the agony aunt in *Agony*?
4. Which football team does Alf Garnett support?
5. Which American writer 'lived' the parts of stand-up comic, trapeze artist, boxer, etc., for TV?
6. Which British game show is based on charades?

184

1. In *EastEnders*, what and where is Nick Cotton's tattoo?
2. Actor William Moore is married to her and played her husband in *The Liver Birds*. Who is she?
3. Name the Daleks' home.
4. Who has a fairly secret army?
5. In which TV series do you find the Bunkers?
6. Racial groups objected to which variety show starring the George Mitchell Singers?

34

1. Pam and Bobby.
2. Alan Whicker.
3. *Billy Bunter*.
4. *Going Straight*.
5. Sabrina Duncan.
6. *Ready, Steady, Go!*

109

1. Shepherd.
2. Dame Edna Everage.
3. Maureen Lipman.
4. West Ham.
5. George Plimpton.
6. *Give Us a Clue*.

184

1. A bluebird, on his neck.
2. Mollie Sugden.
3. Skaro.
4. Major Harry Truscott (Geoffrey Palmer).
5. *All in the Family*.
6. *The Black and White Minstrel Show*.

35

1. Name the gipsy girl Benny wanted to marry – but who died on their wedding day in *Crossroads*.
2. Who was born in Barnsley and made a million in Australia?
3. Who is the Equalizer?
4. Whose show brought the Roly Polys to television?
5. Who are Sharon Gless and Tyne Daly?
6. Who are Louise the Lamb, Sally the Seal, Willy the Worm and Peregrine the Penguin?

110

1. What was odd about Billy Walker's engagement in *Coronation Street*?
2. Who will never be able to shake off the label 'the thinking man's crumpet'?
3. In which series did Patrick Allen play an adventurer in Morocco?
4. Who played the father in *Bless This House*?
5. Which thriller series starts with instructions delivered on a self-destructing record?
6. Ludovic Kennedy hosts which show about television?

185

1. Name Alexis's dog in *Dynasty*.
2. Who said, 'Schhhh,' in dozens of commercials?
3. Who played the one and only Phyllis Dixey?
4. Name George Burns's wife and screen partner.
5. Who starred in the title role of *Johnny Staccato*?
6. In *Upstairs Downstairs*, how many times was Elizabeth Bellamy married?

35

1. Maureen.
2. Michael Parkinson.
3. Edward Woodward.
4. Les Dawson.
5. Cagney and Lacey.
6. Animals who appeared with Muffin the Mule.

110

1. He was engaged to Deirdre Barlow twice.
2. Joan Bakewell.
3. *Crane*.
4. Sid James.
5. *Mission Impossible*.
6. *Did You See . . . ?*

185

1. Rio.
2. William Franklyn.
3. Lesley-Anne Down.
4. Gracie Allen.
5. John Cassavetes.
6. Twice.

36

1. Name the gamekeeper in *Emmerdale Farm*
2. Who is Mrs Desmond Wilcox?
3. Susan Woolridge played Daphne Manners in which period drama?
4. Name the Goodies.
5. Who is Fred Flintstone's neighbour?
6. Which is the brewery that supplies the Rovers Return (*Coronation Street*)?

111

1. In *Dallas*, Sue Ellen was a beauty queen when she met J.R. What was her title?
2. Of whom was it said, 'He rose without trace'?
3. What was very odd about the Dennis Potter play *Blue Remembered Hills*?
4. What do Julia Hills, Rory McGrath, Jimmy Mulville, Philip Pope and Tony Robinson have in common?
5. Who plays Quincy?
6. Which comic devised *Bullseye*?

186

1. What naughty film did Pete film with his video camera in *EastEnders*?
2. Which member of the Goodies is a bird-watching fanatic?
3. Name the thriller in which Tom Bell plays the hard man out of prison and out to find the man who shopped him.
4. Which curly comic once had a double act with Jerry Stevens?
5. Who produced and hosted America's *Candid Camera*?
6. In which year did Channel Four go on the air?

36

1. Seth Armstrong.
2. Esther Rantzen.
3. *The Jewel in the Crown*.
4. Graeme Garden, Bill Oddie, Tim Brooke-Taylor.
5. Barney Rubble.
6. Newton and Ridley.

111

1. Miss Texas.
2. David Frost.
3. Adults played the seven-year-olds.
4. *Who Dares Wins*.
5. Jack Klugman.
6. Norman Vaughan.

186

1. His wife, Kath, in her underwear.
2. Bill Oddie.
3. *Out*.
4. Lennie Bennett.
5. Allen Funt.
6. 1982.

37

1. In *Crossroads*, who or what were Euripides, Mercury and Jupiter?
2. Whose bottom is as famous as her face when she is treasure-hunting?
3. What did the hero suffer from in *The Singing Detective*?
4. Which down-under comic advertised lager with lines like 'Strewth! That bloke's not wearing his strides!'?
5. Who played Amos Burke, Secret Agent?
6. What was Edna Cross addicted to in *Brookside*?

112

1. Who helped with the saucy bits when Mavis Riley tried her hand at writing a play in *Coronation Street*?
2. Who gets his nickname by adding 'bum' to his surname?
3. Which American actress played Jennie, Lady Randolph Churchill?
4. Who achieved fame with a four-legged partner after splitting with his brother Mike?
5. Who does Gary Burghoff play in *M*A*S*H*?
6. What is the X Y Z in the thriller series *The X Y Z Man*?

187

1. Who was in an asylum for a while in *Dynasty*?
2. Who became a TV personality, thanks to her doggerel poetry, after appearing on *Opportunity Knocks*?
3. At the end of Jeffrey Archer's *First Among Equals*, who got into Number Ten – a Socialist or a Conservative?
4. Who played the number-one screw in *Porridge*?
5. Who played Bronco?
6. In which series does Ray Brooks play a compulsive gambler?

37

1. Miss Tatum's cat and two dogs.
2. Anneka Rice.
3. Psoriasis (a skin disease).
4. Paul Hogan.
5. Gene Barry.
6. Gambling.

112

1. Victor Pendlebury.
2. Jeremy Beadle.
3. Lee Remick.
4. Bernie Winters.
5. Radar.
6. An extra chromosome.

187

1. Sammy Jo Reece (and Claudia Blaisdell).
2. Pam Ayres.
3. A Socialist.
4. Fulton MacKay.
5. Ty Hardin.
6. *Big Deal*.

38

1. Where did Lucy's parents, Val and Gary Ewing, go to live (*Dallas*)?
2. Name the soap-opera star whose late husband could be filmed only from the waist up on America's *Ed Sullivan Show*?
3. Where did the Tenko women go for their reunion?
4. Despite his surname, who is red-hot with his rubber face?
5. Name the trailmaster in *Wagon Train*.
6. In which city is private eye Joe Mannix based?

113

1. Name Donald Hinton's job (*Emmerdale Farm*).
2. Name the former *Blue Peter* presenter who had a dog called Shep.
3. Who died while making the second series of *Auf Wiedersehen, Pet*?
4. *Robin's Nest* and *George and Mildred* were spin-offs from which sitcom?
5. Who played the title role in *The Flying Nun*?
6. Which long-running police series was based on the film *The Blue Lamp*?

188

1. What business did Lofty, Kelvin and Ian start in *EastEnders*?
2. Which TV personality once had a number-one hit with 'The Man From Laramie'?
3. A bowler hat and furled umbrella are which nattily dressed secret agent's trademark?
4. In which department at Grace Brothers do Mrs Slocombe and Miss Brahms work?
5. In *Bewitched*, how does the attractive witch switch on the magic?
6. In which private-eye series is there a character called Kookie?

38

1. Knots Landing.
2. Priscilla Presley (Jenna in *Dallas*).
3. Singapore.
4. Phil Cool.
5. Major Adams.
6. Los Angeles.

113

1. Vicar.
2. John Noakes.
3. Gary Holton.
4. *Man About the House*.
5. Sally Field.
6. *Dixon of Dock Green*.

188

1. Machine-knitting.
2. Jimmy Young.
3. John Steed (*The Avengers*).
4. Ladies' underwear (*Are You Being Served?*).
5. By twitching her nose.
6. *77 Sunset Strip*. (Kookie is played by Ed Byrnes.)

39

1. Whom did Benny offer to marry, even though she was pregnant by another man in *Crossroads*?
2. Which marathon runner fixes it?
3. Compo, Clegg and Foggy are characters in which series?
4. Name Bernie Winters's four-legged friend.
5. Who are the Clampett family?
6. Who is often abused as a 'silly old moo'?

114

1. In *Coronation Street*, Deirdre had a naughty weekend in the Lake District while she was still married to Ray Langton – with whom?
2. Which chat-show host's programme opened with his driving into the studio in an E-Type Jaguar?
3. Who played spycatcher George Smiley in *Smiley's People*?
4. In which series would you find Rodney and Del Boy?
5. In which town do the Flintstones live?
6. Which puppeteer created Sooty?

189

1. In *Dynasty*, what disguise did Dex and Alexis use to get out of Moldavia?
2. Whose catchphrase – and the title of his TV show – was 'Before your very eyes'?
3. Which actor won a top award for his performance as the detective investigating the death of his daughter in *Edge of Darkness*?
4. Who is 'the one with the short fat hairy legs'?
5. Who played a Nixonesque president in *Washington: Behind Closed Doors*?
6. Which pop show hooted a klaxon for a miss and rang a bell for a hit?

39

1. Josie Welsh.
2. Jimmy Savile.
3. *Last of the Summer Wine*.
4. Schnorbitz.
5. The Beverly Hillbillies.
6. Else Garnett (*Till Death Us Do Part*).

114

1. Ken Barlow.
2. Simon Dee.
3. Sir Alec Guinness.
4. *Only Fools and Horses*.
5. Bedrock.
6. Harry Corbett.

189

1. Doctor and nurse.
2. Arthur Askey.
3. Bob Peck.
4. Ernie Wise.
5. Jason Robards.
6. *Juke Box Jury*.

40

1. Name Ray Krebbs's father in *Dallas*.
2. Who was Mr Pastry?
3. In which singing-and-dancing drama did Gemma Craven rouge her nipples?
4. Who cracked the first of thousands of jokes on *The Comedians*? (Clue: It's the way he tells 'em.)
5. Who invented the Muppets?
6. In which town does Postman Pat do his rounds?

115

1. In *Emmerdale Farm*, why did Joe Sugden return to Beckindale?
2. Who does a wonderful impersonation of Margaret Thatcher despite a 41-inch bust?
3. Name the character who is thawed out after more than sixty years to deal with twentieth-century villains?
4. Who is E. L. Wisty?
5. In which Western does Hawkeye appear?
6. Which long-running TV ad campaign has been called a 'simian sitcom'?

190

1. Where was Lofty sitting when he proposed to Michelle in *EastEnders*?
2. Who are Joy, Babs and Teddie?
3. Name the play based on actress Coral Browne's real-life chance meeting with former spy Guy Burgess in Moscow?
4. Who co-wrote scripts such as *Whack-O!* and then discovered it would be all right on the night?
5. Sable is a nickname – what is her real name (*The Colbys*)?
6. Little Weed appeared alongside whom?

40

1. Jock Ewing.
2. Richard Hearne.
3. *Pennies from Heaven*.
4. Frank Carson.
5. Jim Henson.
6. Greendale.

115

1. For the funeral of his grandfather.
2. Faith Brown.
3. Adam Adamant.
4. Peter Cook.
5. *The Last of the Mohicans*.
6. Brooke Bond PG Tips.

190

1. On a park bench in Albert Square.
2. The Beverley Sisters.
3. *An Englishman Abroad*.
4. Denis Norden.
5. Sabella.
6. Bill and Ben, the Flowerpot Men.

41

1. In *Crossroads*, Diane Hunter has an illegitimate son, Nicholas, as the result of an affair with a pop star. Name him.
2. Who helped the BBC launch its daytime schedules after resigning as a Labour MP?
3. What business were the Brothers in?
4. Who played the gloomy undertaker in *Dad's Army*?
5. Name Howdy Doody's brother.
6. In which year did the BBC start its television service?

116

1. Whose was the first wedding in *Coronation Street*?
2. Who were Davy Jones, Mike Nesmith, Mickey Dolenz and Peter Tork?
3. Name the series in which a scientist solves crimes by making himself invisible.
4. Which clerical comedy was set at St Jude's?
5. What is printed on Paladin's calling card?
6. Which game show links celebrities and members of the public with the same star sign?

191

1. Which *Dynasty* star loosens his tie in the opening sequence?
2. Who was Larry Grayson's attractive sidekick on *The Generation Game*?
3. Whose firearm was a .30–40 sawed-off carbine called Mare's Laig?
4. Who was always yelling, 'Everybody out!'?
5. Which series is set at the San Francisco Memorial Hospital?
6. Name Bo and Luke's car in *The Dukes of Hazzard*.

41

1. Frank Adams.
2. Robert Kilroy-Silk.
3. Road haulage.
4. John Laurie.
5. Double Doody.
6. 1936.

116

1. The wedding of Joan Walker (daughter of Jack and Annie Walker) to teacher Gordon Davis, in March 1961.
2. The Monkees.
3. *The Invisible Man*.
4. *Bless Me, Father*.
5. A chess knight – and the words 'Have Gun – Will Travel'.
6. *The Zodiac Game*.

191

1. Jack Coleman.
2. Isla St Clair.
3. Josh Randall (Steve McQueen) in *Wanted: Dead or Alive*.
4. Paddy (Miriam Karlin) in *The Rag Trade*.
5. *Trapper John, MD*.
6. General Lee.

42

1. Who likes to have breakfast outdoors in *Dallas*?
2. A woolly hat was the trademark of which Monkee?
3. Which thriller series has a character called B. A. – standing for Bad Attitude?
4. Who says, 'Give order – thank you please!'?
5. In which series would you find a car called K.I.T.T?
6. Who is the captain of Hill Street precinct?

117

1. Name the manager of N Y Estates in *Emmerdale Farm*.
2. Who joked that she should have won Best Supporting Bra award for her starring role as a southern belle in *North and South*?
3. In which series do you find Robin Masters's estate?
4. Whose usual greeting to a girl was 'Good evening, young sir'?
5. Who had an eye-scratching, hair-pulling fight in a swimming pool in *Dynasty*?
6. Which thriller series has a character called Howling Mad?

192

1. Who stripped down to a red satin G-string at the Queen Vic's ladies' night in *EastEnders*?
2. Name the host of the quiz show *Pass the Buck*.
3. Who plays gambling Robby Box in *Big Deal*?
4. Who upstaged the stars by signing off with 'Thank you for watching my little show. Good night, and I love you all'?
5. Which series features a father-and-daughter police team?
6. Who was 'brought back from the dead' in *Dallas*?

A

42

1. J.R.
2. Mike Nesmith.
3. *The A-Team*.
4. Colin Crompton (chairman of the Wheeltappers and Shunters Social Club).
5. *Knight Rider*.
6. Frank Furillo.

117

1. Alan Turner.
2. Lesley-Anne Down.
3. *Magnum P.I.*
4. Eric Morecambe.
5. Krystle and Alexis.
6. *The A-Team*.

192

1. Fabulous Frankie (Frankie Jakema).
2. George Layton.
3. Ray Brooks.
4. Janet Webb – at the end of *Morecambe and Wise*.
5. *T. J. Hooker*.
6. Bobby Ewing (Patrick Duffy).

43

1. In *Crossroads*, how did Sandy Richardson end up in a wheelchair?
2. Which singer and celebrity panellist had her first hit record with 'Touch Me'?
3. In which mini-series did Lindsay Wagner open a posh Beverly Hills shop?
4. Who is the Virgin of the Valleys in *Hi-de-Hi!*?
5. Where is *The Equalizer* set?
6. Name the host of *Masterteam*.

118

1. Who had a pigeon called Gilbert, which was eaten by Minnie Caldwell's cat in *Coronation Street*?
2. Who is Don Johson's co-star in *Miami Vice*?
3. Who played the title role in *Jesus of Nazareth*?
4. Name Frankie Howerd's character in *Up Pompeii*.
5. Who live at 518 Crestview Drive?
6. In *Coronation Street*, who fostered two black children in the mid-1970s.

193

1. Who hired psychic Jason Dehner in *Dynasty*?
2. Which wrestler and TV personality has the unlikely sounding real name of Shirley Crabtree?
3. What was the jewel in the crown?
4. Who or what is Dino in *The Flintstones*?
5. Who are Crockett and Tubbs?
6. Which long-running kids' programme was first introduced by a former Miss Great Britain called Leila Williams?

43

1. He was involved in a car crash after a wedding in 1972.
2. Samantha Fox.
3. *Scruples.*
4. Gladys Pugh (Ruth Madoc).
5. New York.
6. Angela Rippon.

118

1. Albert Tatlock.
2. Philip Michael Thomas.
3. Robert Powell.
4. Lurcio.
5. The Beverly Hillbillies (the Clampett family).
6. Ernest and Emily Bishop.

193

1. Blake.
2. Big Daddy.
3. A painting of Queen Victoria sitting on the Indian throne.
4. Their pet dinosaur.
5. The detectives in *Miami Vice.*
6. *Blue Peter.*

Q

44

1. In *Dallas*, what family gathering is an annual Ewing tradition?
2. Who invites the audience to 'pin back your lugholes' before reciting doggerel?
3. Who played Miss Bluebell?
4. Name the show in which the main character is always saying, 'Ooh, Betty!'?
5. In which medical thriller series would you expect to find Danny's Place?
6. Who ran Queenie's Castle?

119

1. What does N Y Estates stand for in *Emmerdale Farm*?
2. Which ventriloquist has a dummy called Nookie Bear?
3. Which play, starring Patricia Hayes, was an examination of vagrancy?
4. Who always gets a laugh when he says, 'I'm free!'?
5. What do Morgan Fairchild, Francine Tacker and Priscilla Presley have in common?
6. Name the town in *Dad's Army*.

194

1. What is Ian Beale's favourite sport in *EastEnders*?
2. Which funny lady was always forgetting the question?
3. Which infamous highwayman has been played by Richard O'Sullivan?
4. Where did Alf and Else Garnett retire to?
5. Name the two series with the character Oscar Goldman.
6. Who came between Cathy Gale and Tara King?

44

1. Miss Ellie's barbecue.
2. Cyril Fletcher.
3. Carolyn Pickles.
4. *Some Mothers Do 'Ave 'Em.*
5. *Quincy.*
6. Diana Dors.

119

1. North Yorkshire Estates.
2. Roger de Courcey.
3. *Edna, the Inebriate Woman.*
4. John Inman.
5. They have all played Jenna Wade in *Dallas.*
6. Walmington-on-Sea.

194

1. Boxing.
2. Goldie Hawn (in *Rowan and Martin's Laugh-in*).
3. Dick Turpin.
4. Easbourne.
5. *The Six Million Dollar Man* and *The Bionic Woman.*
6. Emma Peel. (All were John Steed's sidekicks in *The Avengers.*)

45

1. Name the policeman who proposed to Diane in *Crossroads*.
2. Name the consumer journalist who presented *Checkpoint* on radio and TV.
3. Whose voice is the never-seen Robin Masters in *Magnum P.I.*?
4. Who asks for 'permission to speak' in *Dad's Army*?
5. In *Hill Street Blues*, what do Frank Furillo and John LaRue have in common?
6. Who is the child who is seen most often on British TV?

120

1. In *Coronation Street*, what did Jerry Booth name the boat he built in Len Fairclough's backyard?
2. Which astrologer reckoned his future was with BBC's *Breakfast Time* and later switched to *TV-am*?
3. Which British director has made a name for himself with improvised comedy dramas such as *Abigail's Party*?
4. Who immortalized the Phantom Raspberry Blower of London?
5. What does Johnny Staccato do when he isn't busy sleuthing?
6. Name the fly-on-the-wall documentary about the Thames Valley police.

195

1. Who was Krystle involved with before marrying Blake in *Dynasty*?
2. Name the Anglo-American journalist who won awards for his mammoth documentary series *America*.
3. What drama series do Robin Ellis, Angharad Rees, Jill Townsend and Ralph Bates have in common?
4. Where did five go mad?
5. What colour are the stripes on the A-Team's van?
6. In *Brookside*, who took Heather to Portugal for the weekend?

45

1. Steve Carter.
2. Roger Cook.
3. Orson Welles.
4. Lance Corporal Jones (Clive Dunn).
5. They are both alcoholics.
6. Carol Hersee, the girl on the BBC TV test card.

120

1. *Shangri-La*.
2. Russell Grant.
3. Mike Leigh.
4. The Two Ronnies.
5. He is a jazz pianist.
6. *Police*.

195

1. Matthew Blaisdell.
2. Alistair Cooke.
3. *Poldark*, set in eighteenth-century Cornwall.
4. Dorset.
5. Red.
6. Tom Curzon.

46

1. What was Takapa, which Jock and Ellie fought over in *Dallas*?
2. Who is the real-life weight-lifting and keep-fit fanatic of *Coronation Street*?
3. Name the highly popular drama series about a family of London merchants in the late nineteenth and early twentieth century.
4. Which comedy series featured a spoof soap opera called *WestEnders*?
5. Who played the part-Indian blacksmith in *Gunsmoke*?
6. What is the make of the extraordinary car in *Knight Rider*?

121

1. Who 'hears all, sups all, says nowt' in *Emmerdale Farm*?
2. Which movie and music quizmaster is the son of a famous comic?
3. Name the drama series, starring Tom Conti, about a group of people who met at Cambridge in the 1950s.
4. In which series would you expect to find René's café?
5. Name the series, about a dippy Jewish girl in New York, that emerged from *The Mary Tyler Moore Show*.
6. Which BBC play about Borstal life was rejected by the BBC because it was too violent but was later seen as a movie on Channel Four?

196

1. What was pensioner Reg Cox's hobby in *EastEnders*?
2. Which *Dad's Army* regular wrote *The Ghost Train*?
3. What was the relationship, for almost all of the time, between Paul Nicholas and Jan Francis?
4. Which comic has a full house?
5. Which private eye has a lovely sidekick called C.J.?
6. Name the heroin addict in *Brookside*.

46

1. A plot of wilderness land.
2. Christopher Quinten.
3. *The Forsyte Saga*.
4. *Coming Next . . .*
5. Burt Reynolds.
6. It is a Pontiac Firebird Trans-Am.

121

1. Walter.
2. Robin Ray.
3. *The Glittering Prizes*.
4. *'Allo 'Allo!*
5. *Rhoda*.
6. *Scum*.

196

1. Collecting Nazi war souvenirs.
2. Arnold Ridley (Private Godfrey).
3. Just good friends (playing Vince and Penny).
4. Bob Monkhouse.
5. Matt Houston.
6. Nicholas Black.

47

1. Name the girl terrorist who became involved with David Hunter's son Chris in *Crossroads*.
2. Which *EastEnders* star had a chart hit with 'Every Loser Wins'?
3. Who did Glynn Edwards play in *Minder*?
4. Which buxom character did Lynda Baron play in *Open All Hours*?
5. In which hospital series is Gonzo a doctor?
6. In which country was the Western series *Whiplash* set?

122

1. In *Coronation Street*, who lost his wife in a fire, and then got a job at the Rovers Return?
2. Who was Britain's first TV cook?
3. Which Australian actor had six wives in one series?
4. Which half hour had a reunion party?
5. Who does Emma Samms play in *The Colbys*?
6. Which games show invariably had a 'cuddly toy' on the conveyor belt?

197

1. Who took over Joseph's job at the Carrington mansion in *Dynasty*?
2. Which bald-headed magician conjured up an egg-head residency as a panellist with Eamonn Andrews?
3. Name the series in which Gemma Jones played a working-class cook who became owner of an exclusive London hotel.
4. Whose show was before your very eyes?
5. What is Sergeant Bilko's first name?
6. Who were the Grove family?

47

1. Simone.
2. Nick Berry (Wicksy).
3. Winchester Club landlord Dave.
4. Nurse Gladys Emmanuel.
5. *Trapper John, MD*.
6. Australia.

122

1. Fred Gee.
2. Philip Harben.
3. Keith Michell in *The Six Wives of Henry VIII*.
4. 'The Reunion Party' was an episode of *Hancock's Half Hour*.
5. Fallon.
6. *The Generation Game*.

197

1. Gerard.
2. David Nixon.
3. *The Duchess of Duke Street*.
4. Arthur Askey.
5. Ernie.
6. Central characters in the pioneering BBC soap opera of the mid-1950s.

48

1. Who, in *Dallas*, has been editor of a fashion magazine, waitress and boutique owner?
2. Who became known as TV's 'number-one egghead' thanks to his series *The Ascent of Man*?
3. Name Jack Rosenthal's TV play that recreated the BBC's dramatic beginning to television broadcasting.
4. What comedy, about an East End tailor's business, do Vince Powell, Harry Driver, Joe Lynch and John Bluthal have in common?
5. Name the spy spoof, starring Don Adams as Maxwell Smart, whose catchphrase was 'Sorry about that'.
6. Who, as its Chief Executive, launched Channel Four?

123

1. To which Continental city did Jack Sugden go to write before returning to Emmerdale to farm?
2. He is known as Dirty Den – but what is his real name?
3. Which TV drama about a Britain devastated by nuclear attack was transmitted twenty years after it was made?
4. Whose catchphrase was 'You lucky people'?
5. Which sitcom do Judd Hirsch, Jeff Conway and Danny de Vita have in common?
6. What is the TV significance of 2 November 1936?

198

1. What nationality is Ali in *EastEnders*?
2. How is American singer and comedian Dino Crocetti, who puts on a good act of being drunk, better known?
3. Which British series starred Charles Korvin as international crimebuster Inspector Paul Duval?
4. Who or what is introduced with the words 'He's ferocious, he's courageous, he's the king of the jungle!'?
5. Who played McDermott in *Hotel*?
6. Who or what was Ally Pally?

48

1. Jenna Wade.
2. Dr Jacob Bronowski.
3. *The Fools on the Hill.*
4. *Never Mind the Quality, Feel the Width.*
5. *Get Smart.*
6. Jeremy Isaacs.

123

1. Rome.
2. Leslie Grantham.
3. *The War Game.*
4. Tommy Trinder.
5. *Taxi.*
6. The birth of BBC TV.

198

1. Turkish-Cypriot.
2. Dean Martin.
3. *Interpol Calling.*
4. Lenny the Lion.
5. James Brolin.
6. Alexandra Palace, the original home of BBC television.

49

1. What made Mrs Irene Bailey an unusual guest at Crossroads Motel?
2. Which American comedienne lived at London's Savoy Hotel in real life while employing a butler on television?
3. Who played banker husband and showbiz wife in *Telford's Change*?
4. In which sitcom would you find Fenner's Fashions?
5. What's the code name of the secret agent who teamed up with Mrs King?
6. Who is the B B C's voice of tennis?

124

1. In *Coronation Street*, who are Irma, Trevor, Tony and Silvia?
2. Who is the B B C's Scottish voice of rugby?
3. Who played a he-man seaman in *Triangle* and, later, a Great Train Robber?
4. Which music-hall comic's life was turned into the drama series *Funny Man*?
5. What's Jim Rockford's father's nickname in *The Rockford Files*?
6. In which cartoon series would you find Jellystone National Park?

199

1. How did major-domo Joseph kill himself in *Dynasty*?
2. Who is the outrageous Divine Miss M?
3. How did Eli Nathenson grow up to be David Threlfall?
4. Who are the business-like Two Rons?
5. What do Peter Duel and Roger Davis have in common?
6. Who are Francis Wilson, Jack Scott and Michael Fish?

49

1. She committed suicide.
2. Elaine Stritch.
3. Peter Barkworth and Hannah Gordon.
4. *The Rag Trade*.
5. Scarecrow.
6. Dan Maskell.

124

1. The children of Hilda and Stan Ogden.
2. Bill McLaren.
3. Larry Lamb.
4. Jimmy Jewel.
5. Rocky.
6. *Yogi Bear*.

199

1. He shot himself in the head.
2. Bette Midler.
3. They played the younger and older Leslie Titmuss in *Paradise Postponed*.
4. (Gareth) Hale and (Norman) Pace.
5. Both played Joshua Smith in *Alias Smith and Jones*.
6. TV weathermen.

50

1. In *Dallas*, which of Sue Ellen's lovers became impotent?
2. Which *Z Cars* cop later won an Oscar?
3. Black Bess was whose horse?
4. How are Mr and Mrs Tough better known?
5. Who is Sergeant Bilko's commanding officer?
6. Name Perry Mason's secretary.

125

1. Name the mother of Matt Skilbeck's first wife, Peggy, in *Emmerdale Farm*.
2. Which theatrical dame walked off with the awards for her role in *The Jewel in the Crown*?
3. What is Vince's surname in the series *Just Good Friends*?
4. What is Buster Merryfield's role in *Only Fools and Horses*?
5. Who is the captain of the cruise ship in *The Love Boat*?
6. Name the ex-Archers producer who created more drama off-screen than on when he arrived at Crossroads Motel.

200

1. Why was baby Martin's christening postponed in *EastEnders*?
2. Which sports commentator's boobs earn him a regular slot in *Private Eye*?
3. Who played the hero's girlfriend in *Danger UXB*?
4. Name the comedy series in which Paula Wilcox and Richard Beckinsale played working-class girlfriend and boyfriend?
5. In which series do Gene Barry, Tony Franciosa, Robert Stack and Susan Saint James work for *Fame* magazine?
6. Name ITV's long-running travel programme fronted by Judith Chalmers.

50

1. Dusty.
2. Colin Welland.
3. Dick Turpin's.
4. The Krankies.
5. Colonel Hall.
6. Della Street.

125

1. Anne Sugden.
2. Dame Peggy Ashcroft.
3. Pinner.
4. Uncle Albert.
5. Captain Merrill Stubing.
6. Bill Smethurst.

200

1. He went into hospital suffering from gastro-enteritis.
2. David Coleman.
3. Judy Geeson.
4. *The Lovers.*
5. *The Name of the Game.*
6. *Wish You Were Here.*

51

1. In *Crossroads*, which North African country did Meg visit to open a hotel for Hugh?
2. Which singer often ends his TV shows with the words 'Gwyn eich byd a dymunaf i chwi lawenydd bob amser'?
3. Name the controversial series, starring Meryl Streep, about a Jewish family living under the Nazis.
4. In which series did Rowan Atkinson play the last of the Plantagenets?
5. Name the series dramatizing a century of family history from tribal Africa through slavery to the Civil War.
6. What words introduce *The Twilight Zone*?

126

1. Who shot himself after killing Steve Tanner in *Coronation Street*?
2. Whose dating game is a 'lorra, lorra laffs'?
3. In which mini-series is there a character called Trenton, who ran a car factory in Detroit?
4. In which inky-fingered comedy series did Robert Hardy have two roles?
5. Which soap star played the title role in the TV movie *Rita Hayworth – Love Goddess*?
6. In which annual TV event does Eric Morley announce the results 'in reverse order'?

201

1. Which part does Christopher Cazenove play in *Dynasty*?
2. Who is instantly recognizable when you give him a top hat, cane – and the moonlight?
3. How was the family fortune made in *King's Royal*?
4. Who was Les Dennis's partner who, tragically, died young?
5. Where would you find Rin Tin Tin?
6. What was A for in the Sixties sci-fi drama which introduced the unknown Julie Christie as a beautiful laboratory assistant?

51

1. Tunisia.
2. Tom Jones.
3. *Holocaust.*
4. *The Black Adder.*
5. *Roots.*
6. 'There is a fifth dimension beyond that which is known to man.'

126

1. Joe Donnelli.
2. Cilla Black.
3. *Wheels.*
4. *Hot Metal.*
5. Lynda Carter.
6. The Miss World contest.

201

1. Blake Carrington's evil brother Ben.
2. Frankie Vaughan.
3. By distilling whisky.
4. Dustin Gee.
5. Fort Apache.
6. Andromeda.

52

1. In *Dallas*, at what time is dinner served at Southfork?
2. Name the large presenter of the children's game show *On Safari*.
3. What trade does Peter Bowles ply in *Lytton's Diary*?
4. Which comedienne was not so funny when she threw eggs around *TV-am*'s studio?
5. Who are these soap children – Corrine, Eunice and Billy?
6. In *Ironside*, what is the significance of C12563?

127

1. Who were Sally and Sam (*Emmerdale Farm*)?
2. Which comic-singer was the butt of Morecambe and Wise jokes and became a chat-show host?
3. Which character was Man at the Top?
4. Who are Robin Colvill, Carl Sutcliffe, Maurice Lee, Graham Walker and Albert Sutcliffe?
5. Name the series in which a man, suffering from loss of memory after the American Civil War, tried to find his true identity?
6. Who founded the National Viewers' and Listeners' Association?

202

1. In *EastEnders*, who was the first to be told that Michelle was pregnant?
2. Name the disc jockey known as 'Kid'.
3. Name the series in which Julie T. Wallace had a devilish time with Dennis Waterman.
4. Whose creations are Winston Razzamatazz and Delbert Wilkins?
5. Who saw whom in a shower – an event that turned a whole season of which soap opera into a dream?
6. Who did Francesca Gonshaw play in *'Allo 'Allo!*?

52

1. Promptly at 7 p.m.
2. Christopher Biggins.
3. He is a Fleet Street gossip columnist.
4. Pamela Stephenson.
5. The Tates – in *Soap*.
6. It is the licence number of Robert Ironside's van.

127

1. Peggy's twins, who were killed by a train at a level crossing.
2. Des O'Connor.
3. Joe Lampton.
4. The Grumbleweeds.
5. *A Man Called Shanandoah*.
6. Mary Whitehouse.

202

1. Her grandmother, Lou.
2. David Jensen.
3. *The Life and Loves of a She Devil*.
4. Lenny Henry.
5. Pam saw Bobby in *Dallas*.
6. Maria.

53

1. Who spent their honeymoon in Venice (*Crossroads*)?
2. Which *Auf Wiedersehen, Pet* actor had a chart hit with 'Love Don't Live Here Any More'?
3. Which British actress has played Lady Diana Cooper and Nancy Mitford?
4. Who is the 'plonker' in *Only Fools and Horses*?
5. Which American actor, well-known for playing a shabby TV detective, has a glass eye?
6. Who played the gay drag artist at the Queen Vic in *EastEnders*?

128

1. Who did Australian Ian Latimer have an affair with (*Coronation Street*)?
2. Who is the *Brookside* actor who once played for Liverpool FC?
3. Name the pub in *Howard's Way*.
4. Who are Filthy, Rich and Catflap?
5. Who was pushed into a swimming pool in *Dynasty* before being pushed out of the show?
6. How did Tripper become Slinger?

203

1. Who raped Kirby (*Dynasty*)?
2. Which singer and comedienne hosted a talent show that she had once won?
3. What is the connection between Jim Hacker and Raymond Gould?
4. Which Liverpool comic makes jokes about 'Jermains'?
5. Name the actress and actor who go moonlighting.
6. Which businessman went on telly commercials to describe his product as 'bootiful'?

53

1. Adam and Jill Chance.
2. Jimmy Nail.
3. Patricia Hodge.
4. Rodney (Nicholas Lyndhurst).
5. Peter Falk.
6. Dave Dale.

128

1. Gail Tilsley.
2. Brian Regan (Terry Sullivan).
3. The Jolly Sailor.
4. Nigel Planer, Rik Mayall and Adrian Edmondson.
5. Amanda (Catherine Oxenberg).
6. *Tripper's Day* became *Slinger's Day* when Bruce Forsyth took over from the late Leonard Rossiter.

203

1. Adam.
2. Marti Caine.
3. Both characters became Prime Minister – in *Yes, Prime Minister* and *First Among Equals*.
4. Stan Boardman.
5. Cybill Shepherd and Bruce Willis.
6. Turkey tycoon Bernard Matthews.

54

1. How did Rebecca die in *Dallas*?
2. Which presenter swapped his woolly sweater for a suit and changed back again when he went on holiday?
3. Who came back from a watery grave in *Howard's Way*?
4. Which Irish comic's trademark is a pair of wellies?
5. Who escaped to the mountains, after being unjustly accused of murder, and set up home with a prospector and a bear?
6. Who hosted *Look*, the BBC's wildlife series in the 1950s and 1960s?

129

1. What's the name of Seth Armstrong's pet ferret in *Emmerdale Farm*?
2. Who played the daughter in *Till Death Us Do Part*?
3. Who played the title role in *Marlowe – Private Eye*?
4. For Derek Nimmo, when did life begin in one of his comedy series?
5. Who was Mork's girlfriend?
6. Alan Bleasedale's TV play *The Blackstuff* was the forerunner of which series?

204

1. What football team does Arthur support in *EastEnders*?
2. Which presenter of children's animal programmes was known as the Hot Chestnut Man?
3. Which TV film carried on the story after the *Minder* series ran out of steam?
4. Which TV comedy star was once known as Wild Wilhemina Fifty Fingers?
5. Which cartoon character starred in the last programme before British TV shut down for the Second World War?
6. Which event, on 20 July 1969 (3.46 a.m. on 21 July in Britain) was watched by 600 million viewers around the world?

54

1. In a plane crash, on the way to Houston.
2. Frank Bough, the former *Breakfast Time* host who went on to present *Holiday*.
3. Lynne Howard.
4. Jimmy Cricket.
5. Grizzly Adams.
6. Peter Scott.

129

1. Terence.
2. Una Stubbs.
3. Powers Boothe.
4. Forty (*Life Begins at Forty*).
5. Mindy.
6. *The Boys from the Blackstuff*.

204

1. Walford Town.
2. Johnny Morris.
3. *Minder on the Orient Express*.
4. Victoria Wood.
5. Mickey Mouse.
6. Astronaut Neil Armstrong taking the first human step on the Moon.

55

1. Who befriended Benny and helped him restore his old car in *Crossroads*?
2. Which sports commentator kept his promise on TV after saying during the 1938 FA Cup Final, 'If Preston score now I'll eat my hat'?
3. Who played the title roles in *Edward and Mrs Simpson*?
4. Which American singer-comic had a chorus line called the Gold Diggers in his TV specials?
5. Name the American entertainer who used the catchphrase 'I cried all the way to the bank'.
6. Who has a sidekick called Penfold?

130

1. In *Coronation Street*, whose last words were 'Right, I'm going to St Anne's and I'm not coming back'?
2. Who was dressed in rags in *Tenko* and richly in *The Colbys*?
3. Which sumptuous series led to a fashion for teddy bears among Oxford undergraduates?
4. Which American comedy series was set in Roseville, Kansas?
5. Name Raymond Massey's character in *Dr Kildare*.
6. Who has a sidekick called Erroll?

205

1. Who is known as L.B. in *Dynasty*?
2. Which popular comedy actress occasionally appeared in *Coronation Street* as Nellie Harvey of the Lady Licensed Victuallers?
3. In *Brookside*, how many children does Sheila Grant have?
4. Who played the small suburban man in *No, That's Me Over Here*?
5. Name the star of the classic series *The Honeymooners*.
6. Derek Roy hosted which early British bad-taste game show?

55

1. Joe MacDonald.
2. Tommy Woodruffe.
3. Edward Fox and Cynthia Harris.
4. Dean Martin.
5. Liberace.
6. Dangermouse.

130

1. Ena Sharples (on 2 April 1980).
2. Stephanie Beacham.
3. *Brideshead Revisited*.
4. *Bilko*.
5. Dr Leonard Gillespie.
6. Roland Rat.

205

1. Little Blake.
2. Mollie Sugden.
3. Four.
4. Ronnie Corbett.
5. Jackie Gleason.
6. *People Are Funny*.

Q

56

1. In which county is Southfork Ranch situated (*Dallas*)?
2. Which religious broadcaster earned his nickname 'St Mugg'?
3. Where was *Enemy at the Door* set?
4. Which series of programmes brought together the Monty Python team?
5. Name the series in which George Peppard played a Polish Bostonian working for a 10 per cent finder's fee.
6. Name the BBC's first experimental programme, transmitted twice a day from Alexandra Palace.

131

1. Who crashed into Jackie Merrick's motorcycle and put him into hospital (*Emmerdale Farm*)?
2. Which Canadian covered the consumer beat?
3. Who played the title role in the controversial *Casanova* series in the early Seventies?
4. What character did Andrew Sachs play in *Fawlty Towers*?
5. Name the Munsters' pet bat.
6. Commercially speaking, what do Sir Freddie Laker, Victor Kiam II and Bernard Matthews have in common?

206

1. In *EastEnders*, where did the Fowlers find their missing son Mark?
2. Which farmer and TV personality advertised double-glazing?
3. Who played the boss of the Sandbaggers?
4. Which show had a telephone operator who said, 'One ringy-dingy, two ringy-dingies . . .'?
5. In *M*A*S*H*, what is printed on Klinger's baseball shirt?
6. What is Stefanie Powers's job in *Hart to Hart*?

56

1. Braddock.
2. Malcolm Muggeridge.
3. The Channel Islands.
4. *The Frost Report.*
5. *Banacek.*
6. *Here's Looking At You.*

131

1. Alan Turner.
2. Bernard Braden.
3. Frank Finlay.
4. Manuel.
5. Igor.
6. They are all businessmen who have starred in their own TV commercials.

206

1. Southend.
2. Ted Moult.
3. Roy Marsden.
4. *Rowan and Martin's Laugh-In.*
5. 'Mud Hens'.
6. Author.

57

1. Name Nicola Freeman's spoilt stepson in *Crossroads*.
2. How is Charles Springall better known?
3. In which series did Oliver Tobias play a tough young settler in Australia?
4. Which actor put his stamp on *Dear Mother . . . Love Albert*?
5. Who played the Flying Nun?
6. Where do Yogi Bear and Boo Boo live?

132

1. In *Coronation Street*, what is Bet Lynch's middle name?
2. Name the host of *The Krypton Factor*.
3. What is odd about Dr Who's body?
4. Whose creations are Basildon Bond and Barratt Holmes?
5. Which series begins with the words 'Space – the final frontier'?
6. Which character in *Thunderbirds* has an enormous I Q?

207

1. Who was Nick Toscanni's brother in *Dynasty*?
2. Who played Hot Lips Houlihan?
3. In which series was football played by Dunmore United?
4. What do Sid James, Diana Coupland and Sally Geeson have in common?
5. What is the black American version of *Steptoe and Son*?
6. What does C H i P s stand for?

57

1. Daniel Freeman.
2. Charlie Drake.
3. *Luke's Kingdom*.
4. Rodney Bewes.
5. Sally Field.
6. Jellystone Park.

132

1. Theresa.
2. Gordon Burns.
3. He has two hearts.
4. Russ Abbot.
5. *Star Trek*.
6. Brains.

207

1. Gianni.
2. Loretta Swit.
3. *Murphy's Mob*.
4. *Bless This House*.
5. *Sanford and Son*.
6. California Highway Patrol.

58

1. What happened to Amanda Ewing in *Dallas*?
2. Who starred in the odd-ball 1960s series *The Strange World of Gurney Slade*?
3. Which comedy series was about four alcoholics drying out?
4. Which cartoon character is always asking, 'What's up, doc?'
5. Name the series, starring Buddy Ebsen, in which a retired private eye takes over when his son is killed.
6. Name the comedy series starring Millicent Martin as an air hostess.

133

1. Who was first accused of Harry Mowlam's murder in *Emmerdale Farm*?
2. Who created and starred in *Ripping Yarns*?
3. In which series did The Majestics celebrate twenty-five years on the road?
4. What did *T W 3* stand for?
5. Name the trail boss in *Rawhide*.
6. Norm is the husband of which housewife-superstar?

208

1. What old-fashioned profession did Nick Cotton try to get Mary to take up in *EastEnders*?
2. Which Indian film star had a successful cookery series?
3. What role did Patrick Newall play in *The Avengers*?
4. In which series did Liza Goddard play a piano teacher who falls for her rock star pupil?
5. Who played the lead in *Kung-Fu*?
6. Which American newspaperman was the commentator in *The Untouchables*?

58

1. She became insane and went into an institution.
2. Anthony Newley.
3. *I Woke Up One Morning*.
4. Bugs Bunny.
5. *Barnaby Jones*.
6. *From a Bird's Eye View*.

133

1. Matt Skilbeck.
2. Michael Palin.
3. *Tutti-Frutti*.
4. *That Was The Week That Was*.
5. Gil Favor.
6. Dame Edna Everage.

208

1. Prostitution.
2. Madhur Jaffrey.
3. Mother.
4. *Roll Over, Beethoven*.
5. David Carradine.
6. Walter Winchell.

59

1. Why was Gerry Wheeler jailed in *Crossroads*?
2. Which *EastEnders* star played waterpolo for Scotland?
3. Who played the title role in the BBC production of *Anna Karenina*?
4. Name Richard Beckinsale's character in *Porridge*.
5. Who lived in Bugtussle, Tennessee, before moving to Beverly Hills?
6. In which cartoon series would you find Great Kazoo from the planet Zetox?

134

1. What was Albert Tatlock's old regiment in *Coronation Street*?
2. Name the host of *Busman's Holiday*.
3. Who is Adrian Mole's girlfriend?
4. Why is Scooter allowed to appear on *The Muppet Show*?
5. In which series were Robert Culp and Bill Cosby spies disguised as tennis-players?
6. Name the stuttering, computer-generated chat-show host.

209

1. In *Dynasty*, which country did Fallon go to for her divorce from Jeff?
2. Which unlikely person played the judge in the final episode of *Perry Mason*?
3. Who played the title role in *Unity*, about the Mitford sister who fell in love with Hitler?
4. Name the series in which Timothy West played ruthless mill-owner Bradley Hardacre.
5. Who did Jackie Coogan play in *The Addams Family*?
6. Which talent contest was hosted by Tim Brooke-Taylor and Stan Boardman?

59

1. He raped Miranda Pollard.
2. Ross Davidson (Andy).
3. Nicola Pagett.
4. Godber.
5. The Beverly Hillbillies.
6. *The Flintstones*.

134

1. The Lancashire Fusiliers.
2. Julian Pettifer.
3. Pandora.
4. His uncle owns the theatre.
5. *I Spy*.
6. Max Headroom.

209

1. Haiti.
2. *Perry Mason* author, Erle Stanley Gardner.
3. Lesley-Anne Down.
4. *Brass*.
5. Uncle Fester.
6. *The Fame Game*.

60

1. In *Dallas*, what is Sue Ellen's favourite colour of rose?
2. Which former Goon fronted *It's a Square World*?
3. Who was Ace of Spies?
4. What is the link between the S A S and a Channel 4 late-night comedy?
5. Who played Bronco?
6. Name the comedy stars to whom the Prime Minister said, 'Yes,' in the 1987 New Year's Honour list.

135

1. What did Jack Sugden do with Pat's clothes after her death in *Emmerdale Farm*?
2. Which comic went straight when going gently?
3. Who played the Chinese Detective?
4. What's Robin's surname in *Robin's Nest*?
5. What does the O stand for in *Harry O*?
6. Who went in at the deep end?

210

1. Name the father of Michelle's daughter in *EastEnders*.
2. Who, thanks to a little aid from Concorde, managed to sing live on T V on both sides of the Atlantic in July 1985?
3. In which series was a baby boy called Christopher kidnapped back in 1962?
4. What did Hylda Baker and Jimmy Jewel inherit in *Nearest and Dearest*?
5. Who did James Arness play in *Gunsmoke*?
6. Who were Pinky and Perky?

A

60

1. Yellow.
2. Michael Bentine.
3. Reilly, played by Sam Neill.
4. *Who Dares Wins* is the comedy series – and the SAS motto.
5. Ty Hardin.
6. Nigel Hawthorne and Paul Eddington.

135

1. He burned them.
2. Norman Wisdom.
3. David Yip.
4. Tripp.
5. Orwell.
6. Paul Heiney and Chris Serle.

210

1. Den.
2. Phil Collins.
3. *Coronation Street*.
4. A failing pickle factory.
5. Matt Dillon, Marshal of Dodge City.
6. Twin puppet pigs.

61

1. Who is the Nosey Parker of *Crossroads* who returned after ten years?
2. Who played Colonel Hannibal Smith?
3. Where does Rumpole of the Bailey enjoy a drink?
4. In which series did Irene Handl and Wilfred Pickles fall in love?
5. Wyatt Earp was Marshal of where?
6. Who was Looby Loo's boyfriend?

136

1. Name the school where Ken Barlow taught in *Coronation Street*.
2. Which green-fingered personality presented *Gardening Club* and *Gardening World*?
3. Who played the lead role in an early series of *Ivanhoe*?
4. Who was the odd woman out in *Tiswas*?
5. Who is Boo Boo's best buddy?
6. Who was the bank manager in *Dad's Army*?

211

1. In *Dynasty*, what article of clothing helped establish Dan Cassidy's identity in Singapore?
2. *Animal, Vegetable, Mineral?* made a star of which archaeologist?
3. In which series did Robert Powell find stardom as a scientific watchdog?
4. Who was Arthur Haynes's straight man?
5. Who was *Kung Fu*'s Grasshopper?
6. Whose autobiography was called *Let's Get Through Wednesday*?

61

1. Amy Turtle.
2. George Peppard.
3. Pomeroy's.
4. *For the Love of Ada*.
5. Tombstone.
6. Andy Pandy.

136

1. Bessie Street School.
2. Percy Thrower.
3. Roger Moore.
4. Sally James.
5. Yogi Bear.
6. Captain Mainwaring (Arthur Lowe).

211

1. A belt buckle with the letter 'C' on it.
2. Sir Mortimer Wheeler.
3. *Doomwatch*.
4. Nicholas Parsons.
5. David Carradine.
6. Reginald Bosanquet.

62

1. Who is John Ross III's real father in *Dallas*?
2. Who took over as a *Call My Bluff* team captain when Patrick Campbell died?
3. Name Susan Hampshire's character in *The Forsyte Saga*.
4. What are the first names of the Likely Lads?
5. Name the comedy series about two black boys adopted by a widowed millionaire.
6. What's the connection between 'La, La, La', 'Ding Ding Dong', 'A-Ba-Ni-Bi' and 'Diggo-Loo, Diggi-Ley'?

137

1. Name the policeman in *Emmerdale Farm*.
2. Which son-in-law of a Prime Minister presented a current affairs programme?
3. What was Hine's job in the series of the same name?
4. What are the first names of Cannon and Ball?
5. Where, and in which period, was *The Untouchables* set?
6. What role was Bernard Youens best known for?

212

1. Who stole from the Queen Vic's till in *EastEnders*?
2. Which TV naturalist has a zoo in Jersey?
3. Name the family in *When the Boat Comes In*.
4. Name the series starring Thora Hird as a member of the Salvation Army.
5. Name Nick and Nora's dog in *The Thin Man*.
6. What pop programme came down the line?

62

1. J. R. Ewing.
2. Arthur Marshall.
3. Fleur.
4. Terry and Bob.
5. *Diff'rent Strokes*.
6. They have all been winning entries in the Eurovision Song Contest.

137

1. Sergeant MacArthur.
2. Peter Jay (*Weekend World*).
3. An arms salesman.
4. Tommy Cannon and Bobby Ball.
5. Chicago – during Prohibition.
6. Stan Ogden in *Coronation Street*.

212

1. Sharon.
2. Gerald Durrell.
3. Seaton.
4. *Hallelujah!*
5. Asta.
6. *Six-Five Special*.

63

1. What's Tommy Lancaster's nickname in *Crossroads*?
2. Who was the female presenter of *Ready, Steady, Go!*?
3. Which series was based on the life of politician Shirley Williams's mother?
4. Whose catchphrase is 'And there's more'?
5. Name Roy Rogers's dog.
6. What's on Popeye's arm?

138

1. Who had a Chinese girlfriend called Jasmine Chong in *Coronation Street*?
2. Name the team captains in *Give Us a Clue*.
3. What's the name of the private detective, played by Alfred Burke, in *Public Eye*?
4. Who arouses Compo's passions in *Last of the Summer Wine*?
5. Who played American Nazi, George Lincoln Rockwell in *Roots II*?
6. Name the commander of the Starship *Enterprise*.

213

1. Where did Alexis and Cecil Colby get married in *Dynasty*?
2. Which game-show host appeared in the hard-hitting drama series *Muck and Brass*?
3. Name the series in which Nicholas Ball played an ex-copper turned private detective.
4. Who was the star of *Q5*, *Q6*, and *Q7*?
5. In which former TV incarnation did *Dallas*'s Patrick Duffy have webbed hands?
6. Which pop programme proclaimed, 'The weekend starts here'?

63

1. Bomber.
2. Cathy McGowan.
3. *Testament of Youth*.
4. Jimmy Cricket.
5. Bullet.
6. A tattoo of an anchor.

138

1. Billy Walker.
2. Una Stubbs and Lionel Blair.
3. Frank Marker.
4. Nora Batty.
5. Marlon Brando.
6. Captain James T. Kirk.

213

1. In hospital.
2. Jim Bowen.
3. *Hazell*.
4. Spike Milligan.
5. Patrick Duffy (Bobby Ewing) had webbed hands in *Man from Atlantis*.
6. *Ready, Steady, Go!*

64

1. In *Dallas*, which of the Ewings never drives a car?
2. Which former *Crackerjack* host negotiated the right price to host a successful game show?
3. In which British series did Herbert Lom play a psychiatrist?
4. Who got laughs from 'You lucky people'?
5. Name Lucy's neighbours in *I Love Lucy*.
6. Who were known as the Thunderbird Three?

139

1. Name Alan Turner's long-suffering secretary in *Emmerdale Farm*.
2. Who presented *Zoo Time*?
3. What was David Warner's job in *Hold the Back Page*?
4. Who is the 'titter ye not' comic?
5. Which Western series, about an Arizona rancher and his sons in the late nineteenth century, starred Leif Erickson and Cameron Mitchell?
6. Name the American series, starring David Cassidy, about five singing children touring with their widowed mother.

214

1. In *EastEnders*, why did Naima leave Saeed?
2. Who was Botanic Man?
3. Name the series in which Antony Sher played a left-wing sociologist.
4. Who was Rigsby?
5. Name the series about private detective brothers in San Diego.
6. Who played Steptoe?

64

1. Miss Ellie – she always rides a bicycle.
2. Leslie Crowther.
3. *The Human Jungle*.
4. Tommy Trinder.
5. The Mertzes.
6. The dustcart crew in the hit comedy series
   The Dustbinmen.

139

1. Mrs Bates.
2. Desmond Morris.
3. A sports writer.
4. Frankie Howerd.
5. *The High Chaparral*.
6. *The Partridge Family*.

214

1. She discovered he had been to a prostitute.
2. David Bellamy.
3. *The History Man*.
4. Leonard Rossiter in *Rising Damp*.
5. *Simon and Simon*.
6. Wilfred Brambell.

65

1. Who was Diane Hunter's postman husband (*Crossroads*)?
2. Which former TV inspector became a headmaster?
3. *Take Three Girls* – but which actresses?
4. Which TV husband and wife met in *Happy Ever After*?
5. The hero of which sci-fi series fights evil forces in the twenty-fifth century after being unconscious for over 500 years?
6. Who is the British equivalent of Archie Bunker?

140

1. In *Coronation Street*, who had an affair with Hungarian labourer, Miklos Zadic?
2. Which host of *Cool for Cats* became the voice of wrestling?
3. Who went from *Connie* to *The Colbys*?
4. Who has been laughing all the way to the bank ever since his 'Careless Hands' was a chart hit?
5. Name Richard Roundtree's New York private eye.
6. Diane Deen edited the *Ramsden Reminder* in which series?

215

1. Which world statesman had a walk-on part at the Carousel Ball in *Dynasty*?
2. Who played *Coronation Street*'s Len Fairclough from the start until being written out in a motorway accident in 1983?
3. Name the series with Alan Dobie in the title role as a detective in Victorian London.
4. Oh no, who played Selwyn Froggitt?
5. *Falcon Crest* is located in which Californian valley?
6. Which ITV programme boss is also presenter of a Channel Four public-access programme?

65

1. Vince Parker.
2. Frank Windsor.
3. Susan Jameson, Liza Goddard, Angela Down.
4. Terry Scott and June Whitfield.
5. Buck Rogers in *The 25th Century*.
6. Alf Garnett – he is named Archie Bunker in *All in the Family*, the American adaptation of *Till Death Us Do Part*.

140

1. Emily Nugent.
2. Kent Walton.
3. Stephanie Beacham.
4. Des O'Connor.
5. Shaft.
6. *Foxy Lady*.

215

1. Henry Kissinger.
2. Peter Adamson.
3. *Cribb*.
4. Bill Maynard.
5. Tuscany Valley.
6. Gus Macdonald, STV programme controller and presenter of *Right to Reply*.

66

1. What is Adam Carrington's middle name (*Dynasty*)?
2. Who brought *Civilisation* to our screens?
3. Which series starred Stuart Damon, Alexandra Bastedo and William Gaunt as secret agents with peculiar powers?
4. Who did Prunella Scales play in *Fawlty Towers*?
5. What are the first names of Starsky and Hutch?
6. Which Western series had a character called Trampas, played by Doug McClure?

141

1. In *Dallas*, which Ewings were romantically involved before they discovered they were blood relations?
2. Who hosted *New Faces*?
3. Who is Rumpole of the Bailey's favourite poet?
4. Who is known as 'Parrot-Face'?
5. Who live at 1313 Mockingbird Lane, Mockingbird Heights?
6. How many times a week was *Crossroads* screened when it began?

216

1. In *Emmerdale Farm*, who owned the village shop before Alison Gibbins?
2. Who presented the wildlife series *Look*?
3. Whose band of men came riding through the glen?
4. Which Python brought sketches to an abrupt halt on the grounds that they were too silly?
5. Who or what is Flicka in *My Friend Flicka*?
6. Name *Minder*'s theme tune.

66

1. Alexander.
2. Kenneth Clark.
3. *The Champions*.
4. Sybil Fawlty.
5. David and Kenneth.
6. *The Virginian*.

141

1. Ray and Lucy.
2. Derek Hobson.
3. Wordsworth.
4. Freddie Davies.
5. The Munsters.
6. Five.

216

1. Amy Postlethwaite.
2. Peter Scott.
3. Robin Hood's.
4. Graham Chapman.
5. A horse.
6. 'I Could Be so Good for You'.

Q

67

1. Name Ethel Skinner's dog in *EastEnders*.
2. Which Mrs Bott went on a diet for *TV-am*?
3. Who played the Mayor of Casterbridge?
4. Who was always saying, 'I yam what I yam'?
5. Who was King of the Wild Frontier?
6. Which weekly programme takes a look at the press?

142

1. Who played Doris Luke in *Crossroads*?
2. Who played the title role in *Edward the Seventh*?
3. In which series did funnyman Mel Smith go straight as a bent property developer in the Midlands?
4. To whom was Terry Hall attached?
5. Whom is Caine looking for in every episode of *Kung Fu*?
6. Name the spacecraft flown by Steve Zodiac.

217

1. How did the girls stop Mike Baldwin getting rid of the factory cat in *Coronation Street*?
2. Who presented *Zoo Quest*?
3. Who played the Expert?
4. Which comic hosted *Punchlines*?
5. Robert Young and James Brolin played doctors in which series?
6. What did Bob Danvers-Walker do on *Take Your Pick*?

67

1. Willy.
2. Diana Dors – she was Mrs Bott in *Just William*.
3. Alan Bates.
4. Popeye.
5. Davy Crockett.
6. *What the Papers Say*.

142

1. Kathy Staff.
2. Timothy West.
3. *Muck and Brass*.
4. Lenny the Lion.
5. His brother Daniel.
6. *Fireball XL5*.

217

1. They made it a member of the union.
2. David Attenborough.
3. Marius Goring.
4. Lennie Bennett.
5. *Marcus Welby, MD*.
6. He banged the gong.

68

1. What made Blake go temporarily blind in *Dynasty*?
2. Who hosted *The Sky's the Limit*?
3. What fate befell Lady Marjorie Bellamy in *Upstairs Downstairs*?
4. Which sitcom marked a progression from stand-up comedy for Jim Davidson?
5. In which sci-fi series are the Cylons the enemy?
6. What is the game in the BBC test card?

143

1. Name Pamela Ewing's adopted son in *Dallas*.
2. Who was ITN's first female newscaster?
3. What is the connection between Googie Withers, Katharine Blake and Sarah Lawson?
4. In which series did Sid James and Peggy Mount play employees at a stately home?
5. In which mini-series did Richard Chamberlain star as a priest who falls in love?
6. What was *Coming Out* all about?

218

1. Who is Robert Sugden's godfather in *Emmerdale Farm*?
2. Who starred with his wife Lucille Ball in *I Love Lucy* (and later divorced her)?
3. Name the mini-series, starring Stacy Keach, about a lusty French painter from his mid-twenties to his mid-sixties.
4. *In Sickness and in Health* was the follow-up to which series?
5. Who were Rock Hudson and Susan St James as the San Francisco crimebusters?
6. Which Monkee was a Circus Boy?

A 136

68

1. An explosion in a car park.
2. Hughie Greene.
3. She was aboard the *Titanic*, which sank.
4. *Up the Elephant and Round the Castle.*
5. *Battlestar Galactica.*
6. Noughts and crosses.

143

1. Christopher.
2. Anna Ford.
3. All played governors of the women's prison in *Within These Walls*.
4. *George and the Dragon.*
5. *The Thorn Birds.*
6. Homosexuality.

218

1. Amos Brearly.
2. Desi Arnaz.
3. *Mistral's Daughter.*
4. *Till Death Do Us Part.*
5. *McMillan and Wife.*
6. Mickey Dolenz.

69

1. In *EastEnders*, how did the muggers who attacked Debs make their getaway?
2. Name the husband-and-wife team famous for their underwater series.
3. In which series would you find Number-one Son?
4. Who are the brickies' Erics?
5. Duncan Renaldo found fame as which masked Western hero?
6. Which long-running saga celebrated twenty-five years in 1985?

144

1. Whose ex-wife tried to kill him in *Crossroads*?
2. Who is the connection between *Connections* and *The Day the Universe Changed*?
3. Who played the Nearly Man?
4. In which series would you find a van bearing the legend 'New York–Paris–Peckham'?
5. Which cop's badge number was 714?
6. Name the *Auf Wiedersehen, Pet* theme tune.

219

1. In *Coronation Street*, who did Ernie Bishop play piano for when she resumed her singing career?
2. Which former newsreader has been president of the Royal Society for the Protection of Birds?
3. Who played Richter in *Enemy at the Door*?
4. Who became Mrs Pinner – at last – in Paris on Christmas Day, 1986?
5. What do they have in common: Imogene Coca, Janet Blair, Nanette Fabray, Gisele MacKenzie?
6. Smiley Burnette was the sidekick of which singing cowboy?

69

1. On roller-skates.
2. Hans and Lotte Haas.
3. *Charlie Chan*.
4. Their nickname for Germans in *Auf Wiedersehen, Pet*.
5. The Cisco Kid.
6. *Coronation Street*.

144

1. David Hunter.
2. James Burke.
3. Tony Britton.
4. *Only Fools and Horses*.
5. Sergeant Joe Friday's, in *Dragnet*.
6. 'That's Living Alright'.

219

1. Rita.
2. Robert Dougall.
3. Alfred Burke.
4. Penny, in *Just Good Friends*.
5. They played Sid Caesar's wives in *Your Show of Shows*.
6. Gene Autry.

70

1. How did Krystle lose her unborn baby in *Dynasty*?
2. Who brings us *Entertainment USA*?
3. Who came out of retirement in *Tinker, Tailor, Soldier, Spy* to find the traitor in MI5?
4. In which series is President Reagan usually more interested in his Poppin' Pals than in anything else?
5. What question would you ask Car 54?
6. Whose Indian sidekick was Chingachgook?

145

1. Identify the 'Three Bs' Jock used to keep his clients happy in *Dallas*.
2. Which soccer pundit is sometimes referred to as 'the Chin' or 'the Rabbi'?
3. In which adventure series on the high seas would you find Dan Tempest?
4. Which American comic refers to her husband as 'Fang' in her act?
5. Whose boss is Dr Zorba?
6. Whose catchline was 'What a revoltin' development this is'?

220

1. Who does Richard Thorp play in *Emmerdale Farm*?
2. Name the late actor who was king-pin of the motor pool and leader of men in war and poker.
3. Who has had to fight Ice Warriors, Cybermen, Yetis and Drashigs?
4. Blow the whistle on the whistle-blower in *The Rag Trade*.
5. Who played an ex-naval frogman for hire in *Sea Hunt*?
6. Why did Shirley Abicair have strings attached to her kids' TV performances?

70

1. She miscarried after falling off a horse.
2. Jonathan King.
3. George Smiley.
4. *Spitting Image*.
5. The police series was called *Car 54 – Where Are You?*
6. Hawkeye.

145

1. Booze, broads and booty.
2. Jimmy Hill.
3. *The Buccaneers*.
4. Phyllis Diller.
5. Ben Casey.
6. Chester Riley in *Life of Riley*.

220

1. Alan Turner.
2. Phil Silvers.
3. Dr Who.
4. Paddy (Miriam Karlin), who blew her whistle to bring the workers out on strike.
5. Lloyd Bridges.
6. She played the zither – and sang.

71

1. What naughty number did Angie auction for charity in *EastEnders*?
2. Who was born Gerry Dorsey, but chose to sing under the name of the man who wrote the opera *Hansel and Gretel*?
3. Who played Soames in *The Forsyte Saga*?
4. Who was the Radio Ham?
5. There have been two captains of *Star Trek*'s *Enterprise*. Name them *or* the actors who played them.
6. What route did Tod Stiles and Buz Murdock take in a Corvette?

146

1. Who had a big pools win in *Crossroads*?
2. Who took a similar line to Eamonn Andrews after a ten-year gap?
3. Which member of the *Dad's Army* cast turned traitor?
4. What was the subject matter of the comedy dramas *I Can't See My Little Willie* and *Kisses on the Bottom*?
5. Name the series about three reformed delinquents helping the L A P D.
6. What had Bernard Schwartz to do with *The Persuaders*?

221

1. What was the stage name of the snake-charming stripper who was Dennis Tanner's girlfriend in *Coronation Street*?
2. Who does impressions in persons?
3. Name the strange, string-gloved detective who eventually got a series of his own.
4. Who played the caretaker in *Please, Sir*?
5. What was Pam Ewing's maiden name?
6. Where would you find the Wombles?

71

1. Frilly knickers.
2. Engelbert Humperdinck.
3. Eric Porter.
4. Tony Hancock.
5. Captain Christopher Pike (Jeff Hunter) and Captain James T. Kirk (William Shatner).
6. Route 66. Tod and Buz were played by Martin Milner and George Maharis.

146

1. Jim Baines.
2. David Jacobs. He chaired the 1970s revival of *What's My Line?*.
3. John Le Mesurier. He put in an award-winning performance in the spy drama *Traitor* during the run of *Dad's Army*, in which he played Sergeant Wilson.
4. Seaside postcards.
5. *The Mod Squad.*
6. Tony Curtis, who co-starred with Roger Moore in *The Persuaders*, was born Bernard Schwartz.

221

1. La Composita.
2. Mike Yarwood.
3. Bulman.
4. Deryck Guyler.
5. Barnes.
6. Wimbledon Common.

72

1. Name Alexis's cousins in *Dynasty*.
2. Who is the one man who has been presenter of *One Man and His Dog* from the start?
3. In *Upstairs Downstairs*, who stole a baby from a pram?
4. In which sitcom would you find Gunner Beaumont?
5. Who said, 'Let's be careful out there'?
6. What nationality is the chef in *The Muppet Show*?

147

1. In *EastEnders*, which of Martin Fowler's godparents failed to turn up for his christening?
2. Which Goodie is keen that people should tell the truth?
3. Who played a Married Man?
4. Who got around on a bicycle made for three?
5. Where do Crockett and Tubbs operate?
6. Which game show reaches a climax with its 'showcase showdown'?

222

1. In *Emmerdale Farm*, who lives at Home Farm?
2. Name the host of a six-days-a-week blockbuster of a show.
3. Name Smiley's number-one adversary.
4. George and Mildred who?
5. Who ride in General Lee?
6. Who is the patron saint of television?

72

1. Sable, Francesca.
2. Phil Drabble.
3. Mrs Bridges.
4. *It Ain't Half Hot, Mum*.
5. Sergeant Esterhouse in *Hill Street Blues*.
6. Swedish.

147

1. Den Watts.
2. Graeme Garden.
3. Anthony Hopkins.
4. The Goodies.
5. Miami.
6. *The Price Is Right*.

222

1. Alan Turner.
2. Bob Holness.
3. Karla.
4. Roper.
5. The Dukes of Hazzard.
6. St Clare.

73

1. Name Pauline's baby in *EastEnders*.
2. Which Scouser had a blind date?
3. Who was thirteen and three-quarters?
4. Who played *The Young Ones'* landlord?
5. What are the first names of Crockett and Tubbs?
6. ST 1 was the registration number of whose car?

148

1. Name Charlie Mycroft's toy dog in *Crossroads*.
2. Name the host of *Ask the Family*.
3. Who did Michael Rennie play in the television adaptation of *The Third Man*?
4. Name the Minister for Administrative Affairs who became Prime Minister.
5. In which American city did the real-life court cases of *Circuit Eleven* take place?
6. Why are soap operas so called?

223

1. Name Brian's Australian cousin who Gail had an affair with in *Coronation Street*.
2. Which presenter regards his games show as child's play?
3. Which series starred Patrick Wymark as ambitious businessman, John Wilder?
4. In which comedy series does Ronnie Barker stutter to Lynda Baron?
5. Boss Hogg is a character in which series?
6. In which show were contestants gonged if they said 'Yes' or 'No'?

73

1. Martin.
2. Cilla Black.
3. Adrian Mole.
4. Alexei Sayle.
5. Sonny and Ricardo.
6. The Saint.

148

1. Growler.
2. Robert Robinson.
3. Harry Lime.
4. Jim Hacker.
5. Miami.
6. When daytime serials started in America they were often sponsored by soap manufacturers.

223

1. Ian Latimer.
2. Michael Aspel.
3. *The Power Game*.
4. *Open All Hours*.
5. *The Dukes of Hazzard*.
6. *Take Your Pick*.

74

1. In *Dynasty*, which two people were trapped inside a burning cabin?
2. To whom did Prince Charles admit to talking to plants?
3. Who played the Irish R M?
4. Who doubled up in *Hot Metal*?
5. What character did Burt Ward play opposite Adam West?
6. Who was the private eye who became a ghost visible only to his partner?

149

1. In *Dallas*, of what is 2001 Bryant Street, Dallas, the address?
2. Whose job is a question of sport?
3. Who put in an award-winning performance as Sancho Panza in *The Adventures of Don Quixote*?
4. Who played the headmaster of Chiselbury School?
5. Who played the title role in *T. J. Hooker*?
6. What was Bruce Wayne's secret identity?

224

1. In *Emmerdale Farm*, what is the name of the local custom in which the villagers beat the bounds to drive away evil spirits?
2. Which American comic's theme song is 'Thanks for the Memory'?
3. Name the British actor who played *Dynasty*'s Prince Michael of Moldavia.
4. Name the romantic comedy series starring real-life husband and wife Michael Williams and Judi Dench.
5. Name the dwarf actor who starred in *Fantasy Island*.
6. Which country blanks out its screens on Thursdays?

A

74

1. Krystle and Alexis.
2. Sir Alastair Burnet.
3. Peter Bowles.
4. Robert Hardy.
5. Robin – in *Batman*.
6. Hopkirk – in *Randall and Hopkirk (Deceased)*.

149

1. Ewing Oil.
2. David Coleman.
3. Frank Finlay.
4. Jimmy Edwards – in *Whacko!*
5. William Shatner.
6. Batman.

224

1. The Beckstone Thrash.
2. Bob Hope.
3. Michael Praed.
4. *A Fine Romance*.
5. Herve Villechaize.
6. Iceland.

75

1. In *EastEnders*, why did Mary go to court?
2. Which American funny lady asks, 'Can we talk?'
3. Who played Napoleon in 1963?
4. Which British comic hosted *Get Set, Go*?
5. In which series would you find the blind monk, Master Po?
6. In *Dallas*, who is Sly?

150

1. When she left Crossroads Motel, where did Meg Mortimer go to live?
2. Which Irish lady with the gift of the gab declared, 'We love TV'?
3. Who played Queen Mary in *Edward and Mrs Simpson*?
4. Which comedy show is created by Fluck and Law?
5. Who replaced whom after one episode of *Hotel*?
6. Name the pub dog in *EastEnders*.

225

1. In *Coronation Street*, who thinks she can see into the future by reading tea leaves?
2. Who played Daniel Boone?
3. Who made a professional job of going to the Last Place on Earth?
4. Who was investigative reporter Kevin Turvey in *A Kick Up the Eighties*?
5. What was Davy Crockett's rifle called?
6. Name the series in which Kenneth More played a clerical detective.

75

1. For shoplifting.
2. Joan Rivers.
3. Kenneth Griffith.
4. Michael Barrymore.
5. *Kung Fu*.
6. J.R.'s secretary.

150

1. Australia.
2. Gloria Hunniford.
3. Dame Peggy Ashcroft.
4. *Spitting Image*.
5. Anne Baxter took over from Bette Davis.
6. Roly.

225

1. Hilda Ogden.
2. Fess Parker.
3. Martin Shaw.
4. Rik Mayall.
5. Old Betsy.
6. *Father Brown*.

FOR THE BEST IN PAPERBACKS, LOOK FOR THE

In every corner of the world, on every subject under the sun, Penguin represents quality and variety – the very best in publishing today.

For complete information about books available from Penguin – including Pelicans, Puffins, Peregrines and Penguin Classics – and how to order them, write to us at the appropriate address below. Please note that for copyright reasons the selection of books varies from country to country.

In the United Kingdom: For a complete list of books available from Penguin in the U.K., please write to *Dept E.P., Penguin Books Ltd, Harmondsworth, Middlesex, UB7 0DA*

In the United States: For a complete list of books available from Penguin in the U.S., please write to *Dept BA, Penguin, 299 Murray Hill Parkway, East Rutherford, New Jersey 07073*

In Canada: For a complete list of books available from Penguin in Canada, please write to *Penguin Books Canada Ltd, 2801 John Street, Markham, Ontario L3R 1B4*

In Australia: For a complete list of books available from Penguin in Australia, please write to the *Marketing Department, Penguin Books Australia Ltd, P.O. Box 257, Ringwood, Victoria 3134*

In New Zealand: For a complete list of books available from Penguin in New Zealand, please write to the *Marketing Department, Penguin Books (NZ) Ltd, Private Bag, Takapuna, Auckland 9*

In India: For a complete list of books available from Penguin, please write to *Penguin Overseas Ltd, 706 Eros Apartments, 56 Nehru Place, New Delhi, 110019*

In Holland: For a complete list of books available from Penguin in Holland, please write to *Penguin Books Nederland B.V., Postbus 195, NL–1380AD Weesp, Netherlands*

In Germany: For a complete list of books available from Penguin, please write to *Penguin Books Ltd, Friedrichstrasse 10 – 12, D–6000 Frankfurt Main 1, Federal Republic of Germany*

In Spain: For a complete list of books available from Penguin in Spain, please write to *Longman Penguin España, Calle San Nicolas 15, E–28013 Madrid, Spain*

FOR THE BEST IN PAPERBACKS, LOOK FOR THE

PENGUIN BESTSELLERS

Dreams of Other Days   Elaine Crowley

'A magnificent and unforgettable story of love, rebellion and death. 'You will never forget Katy and the people of her place . . . a haunting story' – Maeve Binchy, author of *Light a Penny Candle*

Trade Wind   M. M. Kaye

The year is 1859 and Hero Hollis, beautiful and headstrong niece of the American consul, arrives in Zanzibar. It is an earthly paradise fragrant with spices and frangipani; it is also the last and greatest outpost of the Slave Trade . . .

The Far Pavilions   M. M. Kaye

The famous story of love and war in nineteenth-century India – now a sumptuous screen production. 'A *Gone With the Wind* of the North-West Frontier' – *The Times*. 'A grand, romantic adventure story' – Paul Scott

The Mission   Robert Bolt

History, adventure and romance combine in the most exciting way imaginable in this compulsive new novel – now a major motion picture.

Riches and Honour   Tom Hyman

The explosive saga of a dynasty founded on a terrible secret. A thriller of the first order, *Riches and Honour* captures the imagination with its brutally chilling and tantalizing plot.

The World, the Flesh and the Devil   Reay Tannahill

'A bewitching blend of history and passion. A MUST' – *Daily Mail*. A superb novel in a great tradition. 'Excellent' – *The Times*

To Have and To Hold Deborah Moggach

Viv was giving her sister, Ann, the best present she could think of – a baby. How Viv, Ann and their husbands cope with this extraordinary situation is the subject of this tender, triumphant and utterly absorbing story. Now a powerful TV drama.

Castaway Lucy Irvine

'A savagely self-searching tale . . . she is a born writer as well as a ruthlessly talented survivor' – *Observer*. 'Fascinating' – *Daily Mail*. 'Remarkable . . . such dreams as stuff is made of' – *Financial Times*

Runaway Lucy Irvine

Not a sequel, but the story of Lucy Irvine's life *before* she became a castaway. Witty, courageous and sensational, it is a story you won't forget.

A Dark and Distant Shore Reay Tannahill

'An absorbing saga spanning a century of love affairs, hatred and high-points of Victorian history' – *Daily Express*. 'Enthralling . . . a marvellous blend of *Gone with the Wind* and *The Thorn Birds*. You will enjoy every page' – *Daily Mirror*

A Daughter of the Nobility Natasha Borovsky

A magnificent and spellbinding blend of fiction and history, set in the Russia of Nicholas and Alexandra. 'An enchanting tale that richly recaptures the glorious days of Imperial Russia' – *Booklist*

Love, Honour and Betray Elizabeth Kary

Destined to love, doomed to part, Seth and Charl become part of a seething drama of treachery, tragedy, pain and desire. History and romance entwine spectacularly in this climactic story, as highly charged and memorable as any story told before now.